Study Guide

Fundamentals of Engineering Economics

CHAN S. PARK
AUBURN UNIVERSITY

PEARSON
Prentice
Hall

Pearson Education, Inc.
Upper Saddle River, New Jersey 07458

Acquisitions Editor: Dorothy Marrero
Supplement Editor: Brian Hoehl
Executive Managing Editor: Vince O'Brien
Managing Editor: David A. George
Production Editor: Barbara A. Till
Supplement Cover Manager: Daniel Sandin
Manufacturing Buyer: Ilene Kahn

© 2004 by Pearson Education, Inc.
Pearson Prentice Hall
Pearson Education, Inc.
Upper Saddle River, NJ 07458

The author and publisher of this book have used their best efforts in preparing this book. These efforts include the development, research, and testing of the theories and programs to determine their effectiveness. The author and publisher make no warranty of any kind, expressed or implied, with regard to these programs or the documentation contained in this book. The author and publisher shall not be liable in any event for incidental or consequential damages in connection with, or arising out of, the furnishing, performance, or use of these programs.

Pearson Prentice Hall® is a trademark of Pearson Education, Inc.

Printed in the United States of America

10 9 8 7 6 5 4 3 2 1

ISBN 0-13-143775-5

Pearson Education Ltd., *London*
Pearson Education Australia Pty. Ltd., *Sydney*
Pearson Education Singapore, Pte. Ltd.
Pearson Education North Asia Ltd., *Hong Kong*
Pearson Education Canada, Inc., *Toronto*
Pearson Educación de Mexico, S.A. de C.V.
Pearson Education—Japan, *Tokyo*
Pearson Education Malaysia, Pte. Ltd.
Pearson Education, Inc., *Upper Saddle River, New Jersey*

CONTENTS

Preface

This Study Guide is designed primarily to help you develop a working knowledge of the concepts and principles of engineering economics. Most questions in this guide are structured in multiple-choice format as these types of exam questions are tested on the Fundamentals of Engineering (FE) exam and, increasingly, in introductory engineering economics courses.

The Study Guide follows the outline of *Fundamentals of Engineering Economics*. Chapter 1 outlines the specific contents of this Guide and provides insights into how to best use the Guide in preparing for your course exams as well as the FE exam.

Although I have tried to make the Study Guide as clear and error-free as possible, please direct any suggestions for improving the Study Guide or any errors that are found to me at **park@eng.auburn.edu**. All feedback is greatly appreciated. Any known errors will be posted on the book's website at **http://www.prenhall.com/park**.

CHAN S. PARK
Auburn University

Chapter 1 Getting Started

Each student will use this Study Guide in different ways. This is quite common because both introductory engineering economics courses and individual students' needs vary widely. However, the tips contained in this section should help all students use the Study Guide more effectively, regardless of these differences.

How to Use This Guide

Each chapter contains (1) definitional self-test questions, (2) conceptual self-test questions, (3) self-test problems, and (4) answers and solutions to the self-test questions and problems. You should begin your study by reading the summary in each chapter of *Fundamentals of Engineering Economics*; it will give you an idea of what is contained in each chapter and how it fits into the study of engineering economics. From there, work though each question and problem, consulting the answers and explanations provided. Do not be concerned if your answers differ from ours by a small amount, as it is likely a result of rounding differences.

How to Prepare the Fundamentals of Engineering (FE) Exam

This Study Guide will also help you prepare the FE exam. The FE exam consists of 180 multiple-choice questions. During the morning session, all examinees take a general exam common to all disciplines. During the afternoon session, examinees can opt to take a general exam or a discipline-specific (Chemical, Civil, Electrical, Environmental, Industrial, or Mechanical) exam.

The general exam tests four questions related to engineering economics in the morning session and five in the afternoon session. The specific engineering economics topics covered in the FE exam are
- Annual cost (Chapter 6)
- Breakeven Analysis (Chapter 10)
- Benefit-Cost Analysis (Chapter 12)
- Future Worth or Value (Chapters 2, 3, and 4)
- Present Worth (Chapter 5)
- Valuation and Depreciation (Chapters 8 and 9)

So, if you are using this Study Guide for preparing the FE exam, you may practice the problems contained in the chapters as indicated.

Some examples of questions provided by the National Council of Examiners for Engineering and Surveying (http://www.ncees.org/exams) are shown below. To aid your study, this Guide highlights the critical data provided by each question, isolates the question being asked, and outlines the correct approach in the solution under the headings **Given, Find** and **Approach,** respectively. This convention is also employed throughout the text. This guidance is intended to stimulate student curiosity to look beyond the mechanics of problem solving to explore "what if" issues, alternative solution methods, and the interpretation of the solution.

Sample Test Question 1:

If $200 is deposited in a savings account at the beginning of each of 15 years and the account draws interest at 8% per compounded annually, the value of the account at the end of 15 years will be nearly:

      (a) $6,000   (b) $5,400   (c) $5,900   (d) $6,900

Solution:
     Given: $A = \$200$, $N = 15$ years, $i = 8\%$
     Find: F
     Approach: Note that each deposit is made at the <u>beginning</u> of each year. However, the equal-payment series compound amount factor $(F/A, i, N)$ is based on the end-of-period assumption. To adjust for this timing difference, you may still use the $(F/A, i, N)$ factor, but adjust the resulting F value for the one additional interest-earning period by multiplying it by $(1 + 0.08)$.

$$F' = \$200(F/A, 8\%, 15) = \$5,430.42$$
$$F = \$5,430.42(1.08) = \$5,864$$

Thus, the correct answer is (c).

Sample Test Question 2:

Your county has asked you to analyze the purchase of some dump trucks. Each truck will cost $45,000 and have an operating and maintenance cost that starts at $15,000 the first year and increases by $2,000 per year. Assume the salvage value at the end of 5 years is $9,000 and the interest rate is 12%. The equivalent annual cost of each truck is most nearly

      (a) $31,000   (b) $41,200   (c) $26,100   (d) $29,600

Solution:

Given: $I = \$45,000$, $S = \$9,000$, O&M cost $= \$15,000$ first year, increasing by $\$2,000$ per year, $N = 5$ years, $i = 12\%$

Find: AE(12%)

Approach: Note that there are two kinds of costs: ownership costs (capital costs) and operating costs. The capital costs can be calculated by using the capital recovery with return formula whereas the O&M cost needs to be annualized knowing that it takes a linear gradient series with $G = \$2,000$.

$$CR(12\%) = (I - S)(A/P, i, N) + iS$$

$$= (\$45,000 - \$9,000)(A/P, 12\%, 5) + (0.12)(\$9,000)$$

$$= \$11,067$$

$$AE(12\%)_{O\&M} = \$15,000 + \$2,000(A/G, 12\%, 5)$$

$$= \$15,000 + \$2,000(1.7746)$$

$$= \$18,549$$

$$AE(12\%) = CR(12\%) + AE(12\%)_{O\&M}$$

$$= \$11,067 + \$18,549$$

$$= \$29,616$$

The correct answer is (d).

Chapter 2 Time Value of Money

2s.1 If you invest $2,000 today in a savings account at an interest rate of 12%, compounded annually, how much principal and interest would you accumulate in 7 years?

(a) $4,242   (b) $4,422

(c) $2,300   (d) $1,400.

Solution:

> Given: $P = \$2,000$, $i = 12\%$, $N = 7$ years
> Find: F

$$F = \$2,000(1+0.12)^7 = \$4,421.36$$

2s.2 How much do you need to invest in equal annual amounts for the next 10 years if you want to withdraw $5,000 at the end of the eleventh year and increase the annual withdrawal by $1,000 each year thereafter until year 25? The interest rate is 6%, compounded annually.

(a) $20,000   (b) $106,117

(c) $8,054   (d) $5,000.

Solution:

> Given: Withdrawal series as given, $i = 6\%$, $N = 25$ years
> Find: A

- First find the equivalent total amount of withdrawal at the end of year 10. Since this is a gradient series with $A_1 = \$5,000$, $G = \$1,000$, and $N = 15$, the equivalent worth of this series at year 10 is

$$V_{10} = \$5,000(P/A,6\%,15)+\$1,000(P/G,6\%,15)$$
$$= \$106,116$$

- Since we know how much (V_{10}) need to be saved, we can easily find the annual equal deposits that have to be made.

$$A = \$106,116(A/F,6\%,10)$$
$$= \$8,050.80$$

2s.3 If you make the following series of deposits at an interest rate of 10%, compounded annually, what would be the total balance at the end of 10 years?

End of Period	Amount of Deposit
0	$800
1– 9	$1500
10	0

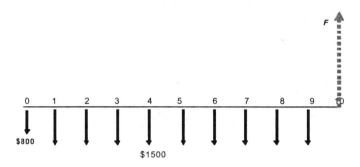

(a) $F = \$22,256$ (b) $F = \$24,481$

(c) $F = \$24,881$ (d) $F = \$25,981$.

Solution:

Given: $A_0 = \$800$, $A = \$1,500$, $i = 10\%$, $N = 10$ years
Find: F

- Note that there are two cash flow components in the series. The first one is a single payment amount ($800) at period 0 and the other is the $1,500 equal payment series. Also we are looking for an equivalent value of these payments at the end of year 10, not year 9. Therefore, we may solve the problem in two steps. First find the equivalent future worth of the single payment at period of 10. Then find the equivalent future worth amount of the $1,500 payment series at the end of year 10.

- Single-payment:

$$V_1 = \$800(F/P,10\%,10)$$
$$= \$2,075$$

- Equal-payment series: First find the equivalent future worth of the series at the end of year 9 and multiply this amount by (1.1) to obtain the value at year 10.

$$V_2 = \$1,500(F/A,10\%,9)(F/P,10\%,1)$$
$$= \$22,406$$

- Total

$$F = V_1 + V_2 = \$24,481$$

2s.4 To withdraw the following $1,000 payment series, determine the minimum deposit (P) you should make now if your deposits earn an interest rate of 10%, compounded annually. Note that you are making another deposit at the end of year 7 in the amount of $500. With the minimum deposit P, your balance at the end of year 10 should be zero.

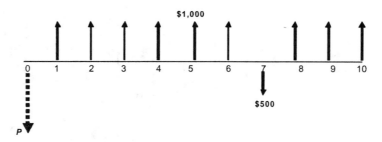

(a) $P = \$4,912$ (b) $P = \$4,465$

(c) $P = \$5,374$ (d) $P = \$5,912$.

Solution:
<u>Given</u>: deposit and withdrawal series given, $i = 10\%$, $N = 10$ years
<u>Find</u>: P

- First find out the equivalent present value of the total withdrawal at period 0. To use the equal-payment series present worth factor, pretend that there will be another withdrawal at period 7 in the amount of $1,000. This assumption allows us to use the (P/A) factor. By subtracting the equivalent present value of the $1,000 added in period 7, we obtain

$$P_{withdraw} = \$1,000(P/A,10\%,10) - \$1,000(P/F,10\%,7)$$
$$= \$6,144.56 - \$513.16 = \$5,631.40$$

- Second, we compute the equivalent present value of the total deposits.

$$P_{deposit} = P + \$500(P/F, 10\%, 7)$$
$$= P + \$256.57$$

- Finally, we solve for P by equating $P_{withdraw} = P_{deposit}$:

$$P_{withdraw} = P_{deposit}$$
$$\$5,631.40 = P + \$256.57$$
$$P = \$5,374.83$$

2s.5 You are planning to borrow $100,000 on a 10-year, 6%, with 10 annual payments. What fraction of the payment made at the end of the second year will represent repayment of principal?

(a) 41.81%   (b) 40.81%
(c) 45.88%   (d) 59.19%

Solution:

Given: P = $100,000, $i = 6\%$, $N = 10$ years
Find: A and portion of the principal payment in the 2nd year

$$A = \$100,000(A/P, 6\%, 10) = \$13,586.80$$

First Year:

$$I_1 = \$100,000(0.06) = \$6,000$$
$$P_1 = A - I_1 = \$7,586.80$$
$$B_1 = \$100,000 - \$7,586.80 = \$92,413.20$$

Second Year:

$$I_2 = \$92,413.20(0.06) = \$5,544.79$$
$$P_2 = A - I_2 = \$8,042.00$$
$$B_2 = \$92,413.20 - \$8,042.00 = \$84,371.19$$

Fraction of the payment:

$$\frac{\$8,042.00}{\$13,586.80} = 59.19\%$$

2s.6 A couple is planning to finance their 5-year-old daughter's college education. They established a college fund that earns 10%, compounded annually. What annual deposit must be made from the daughter's 5th birthday (now) to her 16th birthday to meet the future college expenses shown in the following table? Assume that today is her 5th birthday.

Birthday	Deposit	Withdrawal
5–16	C	0
17		0
18		$25,000
19		27,000
20		29,000
21		31,000

(a) $C = \$3,742$ (b) $C = \$1,978$

(c) $C = \$4,115$ (d) $C = \$3,048$.

Solution:

Given: deposit and withdrawal series given, $i = 10\%$
Find: C

- First establish the base period at period 16 (in fact, you can pick the base period at any period). Then find the equivalent value of the total deposits at the end of period 16.

$$V_{16} = C(F/P,10\%,11) + C(F/A,10\%,10)$$
$$= 21.38C$$

- Second, find the equivalent present value of the future college expenses at period 16.

$$V_{16} = (\$25,000(P/A,10\%,4) + \$2,000(P/G,10\%,4))(P/F,10\%,1)$$
$$= \$80,002.60$$
$$21.38C = \$80,002.60$$
$$C = \$3,742$$

2s.7   If $400 is deposited in a savings account at the <u>beginning</u> of each of 15 years (there are a total of 15 deposits) and the account draws interest at 8% per year compounded annually, the value of the account at the end of 15 years will be most nearly

(a) $11,730   (b) $13,100
(c) $12,130   (d) $12,668

Solution:

Given: $A = \$400$, $i = 8\%$, $N = 15$ years

Find: F

- With the end-of-year deposits:

$$F' = \$400(F/A, 8\%, 15)$$
$$= \$11,730$$

- With the beginning-of-year deposits: Since each deposit has one-extra year of interest earning, the

$$F = \$11,730(1.08) = \$12,668$$

2s.8 What is the present worth of the following income strings at an interest rate of 10%? (All cash flows occur at year end.)

n	Net Cash Flow
1	$11,000
2	12,100
3	0
4	14,641

(a) $37,741   (b) $30,000

(c) $43,923   (d) $32,450.

Solution:

Given: $A = \$200$, $i = 10\%$, $N = 4$ years

Find: P

$$P = \$11,000(P/F, 10\%, 1) + \$12,100(P/F, 10\%, 2) + \$14,641(P/F, 10\%, 4)$$
$$= \$30,000$$

2s.9 Assume that $300 is deposited today, two years from now, four years from now, six years from now, and eight years from now; which of the following statements solves for the future value at the end of year 9? (Assume $i = 10\%$)

(a) $300(F/P, 10\%, 9) + 300(F/A, 21\%, 4)(F/P, 10\%, 1)$
(b) $1062.13(F/P, 10\%, 9)$
(c) Both (a) and (b)
(d) Neither (a) and (b)

Solution:

Given: deposit series given, $i = 10\%$, $N = 9$ years
Find: F

The future worth of the deposit series is
$$F = \$300(F/P,10\%,9) + \$300(F/P,10\%,7)$$
$$+\$300(F/P,10\%,5) + \$300(F/P,10\%,3)$$
$$+\$300(F/P,10\%,1)$$
$$= \$2,504.45$$

The equivalent present value is

$$P = \$2,504.45(P/F,10\%,8) = \$1,062.13$$

The equivalence expression given in (a) is to take advantage of the equal-payment series future worth factor. After the first deposit, the subsequent deposits occur every other year; we may find the equivalent interest rate covering the two-interest period. In other words, a 10% interest earned each year for two years is equivalent to earning 21% interest once for two-year period. Therefore, the expression given in (a) will lead to the correct solution.

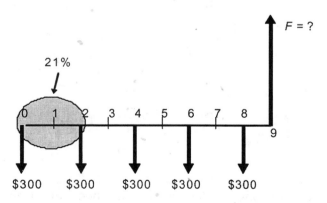

2s.10 What value of X makes these two cash flows equivalent assuming an interest rate of 10%?

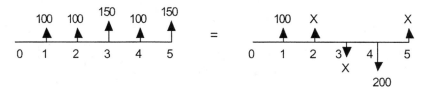

(a) $645
(b) $715
(c) $744
(d) $812

Solution:

Given: cash flow series given, $i = 10\%$, $N = 5$ years
Find: X that makes two cash flow series equivalent

Approach: Anything of this nature is to establish a base period for equivalence calculation. You can pick any time period, period 0 being most common, though. For example, if you pick $n = 0$ as your base period, then compute the equivalent P for both cash flow series, equate them, and solve for unknown X.

- Present value for cash flow series 1:

$$P_1 = \$100(P/A, 10\%, 5) - \$50(P/F, 10\%, 3) - \$50(P/F, 10\%, 5)$$
$$= \$447.69$$

- Present value for cash flow series 2:

$$P_2 = \$100(P/F, 10\%, 1) + X(P/F, 10\%, 2) - X(P/F, 10\%, 3)$$
$$-200(P/F, 10\%, 4) + X(P/F, 10\%, 5)$$
$$= 0.69X - \$45.69$$

- Let $P_1 = P_2$, and solve for X:

$$P_1 = P_2$$
$$\$447.69 = 0.69X - \$45.69$$
$$X = \$715.04$$

2s.11 You want to find the equivalent present worth for the following cash flow series at an interest rate of 15%. Which of the following statements is *incorrect*?

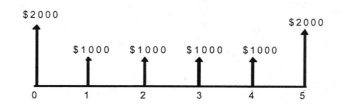

(a) $1,000(P/A, 15\%, 4) + \$2,000 + \$2,000(P/F, 15\%, 5)$

(b) $1,000(P/F, 15\%, 5) + \$1,000(P/A, 15\%, 5) + \$2,000$

(c) $[\$1,000(F/A, 15\%, 5) + \$1,000] \times (P/F, 15\%, 5) + \$2,000$

(d) $[\$1,000(F/A, 15\%, 4) + \$2,000] \times (P/F, 15\%, 4) + \$2,000.$

Solution:

Given: cash flow series given, $i = 15\%$, $N = 5$ years
Find: the incorrect statement
The answer is (d). The correct expression is

$$[\$1,000(F/A, 15\%, 4) + \$2,000(P/F, 15\%, 1)](P/F, 15\%, 4) + \$2,000.$$

2s.12 If you make the following series of deposits and withdrawal at an interest rate of 10%, compounded annually, what would be the total balance at the end of 8 years?

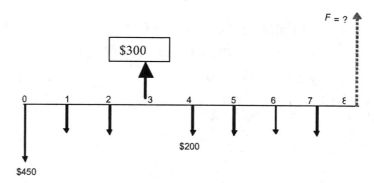

(a) $2,247   (c) $3,052

(b) $2,862   (d) $3,252

Solution:

Given: deposit series given, $i = 10\%$, $N = 8$ years
Find: F

12

$$F = \$450(F/P,10\%,8) + \$200(F/A,10\%,7)(F/P,10\%,1) - \$500(F/P,10\%,5)$$
$$= \$2,246.54$$

2s.13 What value of F_3 would be equivalent to the payments shown in the cash flow diagram below? Assume the interest rate is 10%, compounded annually.

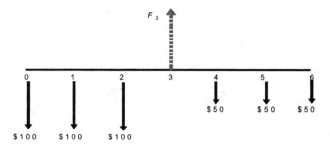

(a) $450   (c) $457

(b) $462   (d) $488

Solution:

 Given: cash flow series given, $i = 10\%$, $N = 6$ years
 Find: F_3

$$F_3 = \$100(F/P,10\%,3) + \$100(F/A,10\%,2)(F/P,10\%,1) + \$50(P/A,10\%,3)$$
$$= \$488.44$$

2s.14 Consider the cash flow series shown below. Determine the required annual deposits (end of year) that will generate the cash flows from years 4 to 7. Assume the interest rate is 10%, compounded annually.

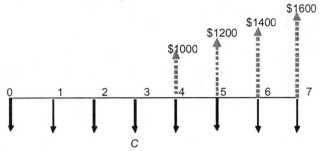

(a) $555   (c) $518

(b) $568   (d) $698

Solution:

Given: cash flow series given, $i = 10\%$, $N = 7$ years
Find: the required deposit series in the amount of C

- Present value of the deposit series:

$$P_{deposit} = C + C(P/A, 10\%, 7) = 5.8684C$$

- Present value of the withdrawal series:

$$P_{withdrawal} = [\$1,000(P/A, 10\%, 4) + \$200(P/G, 10\%, 4)](P/F, 10\%, 3)$$
$$= \$3,039.43$$

- Finding the unknown value, C:

$$5.8684C = \$3,039.43$$
$$C = \$517.93$$

2s.15 If you borrow $20,000 at an interest rate of 10%, compounded annually, with the repayment schedule as follows, what is the amount A?

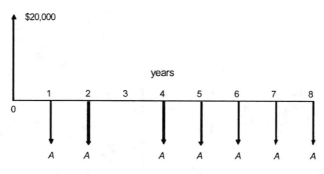

(a) $2,857   (c) $3,345

(b) $3,752   (d) $4,364

Solution:

Given: $P = \$20{,}000$, $i = 10\%$, and $N = 8$ years

Find: the required payment, A

Approach: Since there is one missing payment at the end of year 3, we may modify the repayment series by adding the missing payment and subtracting the missing payment in the same year. The net change is zero, but this will allow us to use the $(A/P,i,N)$ factor.

$$\$20{,}000 = A(P/A,10\%,8) - A(P/F,10\%,3)$$
$$= 5.3349A - 0.7513A$$
$$= 4.5836A$$
$$A = \$4{,}363.40$$

2s.16 Compute the value of V in the following cash flow diagram. Assume $i = 12\%$.

15

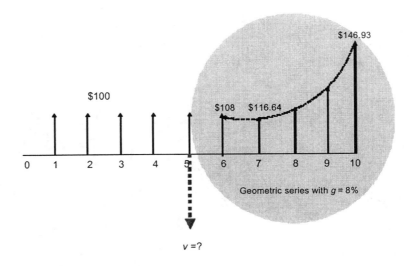

$100

$108 $116.64

$146.93

0 1 2 3 4 5 6 7 8 9 10

Geometric series with $g = 8\%$

$v = ?$

(a) $1,083   (c) $1,260

(b) $1,131   (d) $1,360

Solution:

Given: cash flow series given, $i = 12\%$, $N = 5$ years

Find: the equivalent worth at the end of year 5, V

$$V = \$100(F/A, 12\%, 5) + \$108(P/A_1, 8\%, 12\%, 5)$$

$$= \$635.28 + \$108\left[\frac{1-(1+0.08)^5(1+0.12)^{-5}}{0.12-0.08}\right]$$

$$= \$1,085.05$$

2s.17 What value of C makes the two annual cash flows equivalent at an annual rate of 10%?

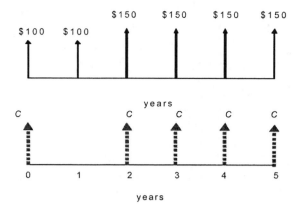

years

0   1   2   3   4   5

years

(a) $99   (c) $160
(b) $150   (d) $220

Solution:

Given: two cash flow series given, $i = 10\%$, $N = 5$ years
Find: C that makes the two series equivalent

$$P_I = \$100 + \$150(P/A,10\%,5) - \$50(P/F,10\%,1)$$
$$= \$623.16$$
$$P_{II} = C + C(P/A,10\%,5) - C(P/F,10\%,1)$$
$$= C + 3.7908C - 0.9091C$$
$$= 3.8817C$$

Let $P_I = P_{II}$ and solve for C.
$$C = \$160.54$$

2s.18 Find the value of X so that the two cash flows below are equivalent for an interest rate of 10%.

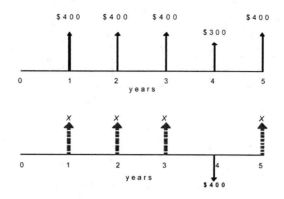

(a) $464   (c) $523

(b) $494   (d) $554

Solution:

Given: two cash flow series given, $i = 10\%$, $N = 5$ years
Find: X that makes the two series equivalent

$$F_{cash\ flow\ 1} = \$400(F/A,10\%,5) - \$100(F/P,10\%,1)$$
$$= \$2,442.04 - 90.91 = \$2,351.10$$
$$V_{cash\ flow\ 2} = X(F/A,10\%,5) - (\$400 + X)(P/F,10\%,1)$$
$$= 6.1051X - 363.64 - 0.9091X$$
$$= 5.1961X - 363.64$$
$$\text{Let } F_{cash\ flow\ 1} = F_{cash\ flow\ 2}$$
$$\$2,351.10 = 5.1961X - 363.64$$
$$X = \$522.46$$

2s.19 Compute the value of F in the following cash flow diagram. Assume $i = 10\%$, compounded annually.

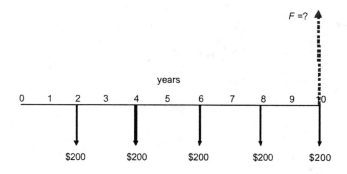

(a) $1,220   (c) $1,517

(b) $1,320   (d) $1,488

Solution:

Given: cash flow series given, $i = 10\%$, $N = 10$ years

Find: F

- Method 1: Find the effective interest rate per payment period, which is over a 2-year period. Then use the following equation to establish the equivalence.

$$i_e = (1 + 0.10)^2 - 1 = 21\%$$
$$F = \$200(F/A, 21\%, 5) = \$1,517.85$$

- Method 2: Find the equivalent annual deposit—in other words, what annual deposits (A') over two years would make a single $200 deposit ($A$) every other year?

$$A' = \$200(A/F, 10\%, 2) = \$95.24$$
$$F = \$95.24(F/A, 10\%, 10) = \$1,517.85$$

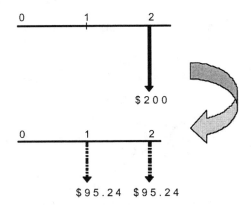

2s.20 Today is your birthday and you decide to start saving for your retirement. You will retire on your 65th birthday and will need $50,000 per year at the end of each of following 20 years. You will make a first deposit 1 year from today in an account paying 8% interest annually and continue to make an identical deposit each year up to and including the year you plan to retire. If an annual deposit of $6,851 will allow you to reach your goal, what birthday are you celebrating today?

(a) 35   (b) 40
(c) 45   (d) 52

Solution:

Given: , Retirement expense = $50,000 per year, deposit amount = $6,851, $i = 8\%$, retirement years = 20 years
Find: N

- The equivalent value of future retirement expenses at the end of 65th birthday:

$$V_{65} = \$50,000(P/A, 8\%, 20) = \$500,840$$

- The number of years required to reach the goal:

$$\$500,840 = \$6,851(F/A, 8\%, N)$$
$$N = 40 \text{ years}$$

Chapter 3 Understanding Money Management

3s.1 You have been offered a credit card by an oil company that charges interest at 1.8% per month, compounded monthly. What is the effective annual interest rate that this oil company charges?

(a) 21.60%   (b) 22.34%

(c) 23.87%   (d) 18.00%.

Solution:

Given: $i = 1.8\%$ per month, compounding frequency = monthly
Find: effective annual interest rate (i_a)

$$i_a = (1+0.018)^{12} - 1 = 23.87\%$$

3s.2 Under the continuous compounding principle, which of the following expressions would allow you to determine the nominal interest rate(r) when the effective annual interest rate is known to be 12%?

(a) $r = e\char`^1.12$
(b) $r = e\char`^0.12$
(c) $r = \text{Log }_e(1.12)$
(d) $r = \text{Log}_e(0.12)$

Solution:

Given: $i_a = 12\%$, compounding frequency = continuous, $K = 1$
Find: nominal interest rate (r)

$$i_a = e^{r/K} - 1$$
$$= e^r - 1$$
$$0.12 = e^r - 1$$
$$e^r = 1.12$$
$$r = \ln 1.12$$
$$= 11.33\%$$

3s.3 Which of the following banks offers you a better interest deal for your deposit?

Bank A: 8.5%, compounded *quarterly*
Bank B: 8.3%, compounded *continuously*

(a) Bank A

(b) Bank B

(c) Indifferent

(d) Not sufficient information to decide.

Solution:

Given: nominal interest rate (r) and compounding frequency

Find: effective annual interest earned by each bank's deposit

Approach: When you compare different interest compounding options, you need to compare them on common basis. In other words, you find out what the effective annual interest rate is under each compounding option.

- Bank A: 8.5% compounded quarterly

$$i_a = (1+0.085/4)^4 - 1 = 8.77\%$$

- Bank B: 8.3% compounded continuously

$$i_a = e^{0.083} - 1 = 8.65\%$$

So, Bank A's offer is a better one.

3s.4 To raise money for your business, you need to borrow $20,000 from a local bank. If the bank asks you repay the loan in five equal annual installments of $5548.19, determine the bank's annual interest rate on this loan transaction.

(a) 11% (b) 11.5%

(c) 12% (d) 27.74%.

Solution:

Given: $P = \$20,000$, $A = \$5,548.19$ and $N = 5$

Find: annual interest rate (i)

$$A = P(A/P, i, N)$$
$$\$5,548.19 = \$20,000(A/P, i, 5)$$
$$(A/P, i, 5) = 0.2774$$
$$i = 12\%$$

22

<u>Comments</u>: Most practical approach is to use either a financial calculator or an electronic spreadsheet such as Excel. A financial function such as RATE($N,0,P,F$) allows us to calculate an unknown interest rate. The precise command statement would be as follows:

$$= \textbf{RATE}\,(5,\ 5548.19,\ -20000)=12\%$$

Note that we enter the present value (P) as a negative number indicating a cash outflow in Excel format.

3s.5 Consider the following bank advertisement appearing in a local newspaper: "Open a Decatur National Bank Certificate of Deposit (CD), and you get a guaranteed rate of return (effective annual yield) of 8.87%." If there are 365 compounding periods per year, what is the nominal interest rate (annual percentage rate) for this CD?

(a) 8.00%   (b) 8.23%
(c) 8.50%   (d) 8.87%.

Solution:

<u>Given</u>: i_a = 8.87%, compounding period = daily
<u>Find</u>: nominal interest rate (r)

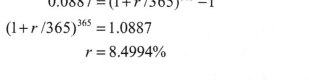

$$i_a = (1+r/M)^M -1$$
$$0.0887 = (1+r/365)^{365} -1$$
$$(1+r/365)^{365} = 1.0887$$
$$r = 8.4994\%$$

<u>Comments</u>: It is much easier to use an Excel's financial command to find the answer. The command, =NOMINAL(8.87%,365), will yield the same result above.

3s.6 What is the future worth of an equal quarterly payment series of $2,500 for 10 years, if the interest rate is 9%, compounded monthly?

(a) $F = \$158,653$ (b) $F = \$151,930$
(c) $F = \$154,718$ (d) $F = \$160,058$.

Solution:

<u>Given</u>: A = $2,500, r = 9% compounded monthly, and N = 40 quarters
<u>Find</u>: F

23

Approach: Whenever the compounding period (monthly) is not the same as the payment period (quarterly), you need to find the effective interest rate that covers the payment period. In our example, you need to find the effective interest rate per quarter.

$$i = (1 + 0.09/12)^3 - 1 = 2.2669\% \text{ per quarter}$$
$$F = \$2,500(F/A, 2.2669\%, 40)$$
$$= \$160,058$$

3s.7 A building is priced at $100,000. If a down payment of $30,000 is made, and a payment of $1,000 every month thereafter is required, how many months will it take to pay for the building? Interest is charged at a rate of 12%, compounded monthly.

    (a) 70   (b) 100
    (c) 121   (d) 132.

Solution:

    Given: $A = \$1,000$, $r = 12\%$ compounded monthly, and $P = \$70,000$
    Find: N

    Approach: With an APR of 12% compounded monthly, the effective interest rate per month is simply 1%.

$$i = 12\%/12 = 1\% \text{ per month}$$
$$\$1,000 = \$70,000(A/P, 1\%, N)$$
$$(A/P, 1\%, N) = 0.0143$$
$$N = 121 \text{ months}$$

Comments: Once again, the Excel command, =NPER(1%,1000,-70000), will
               yield the same result.

3s.8   Susan wishes to make equal end-of-quarterly deposits to her savings account so that at the end of 15 years she would like to have $500,000 in the account. If the account earns 8% interest compounded quarterly, how much should she deposit at the end of each quarter?

    (a) $A = \$4,184$ (b) $A = \$4,384$
    (c) $A = \$4,584$ (d) $A = \$4,784$

Solution:

Given: $F = \$500,000$, $r = 8\%$ compounded quarterly, and $N = 60$ quarters

Find: A

$$i = 8\%/4 = 2\% \text{ per quarter}$$
$$N = 15 \times 4 = 60 \text{ quarters}$$
$$A = \$500,000(A/F,2\%,60)$$
$$= \$4,384$$

3s.9 A series of equal semi-annual payments of $1,000 for 3 years is equivalent to what present amount at an interest rate of 12%, compounded annually? (All answers are rounded to nearest dollars.)

(a) $4,944
(b) $4,804
(c) $4,500
(d) $5,401.

Solution:

Given: $A = \$1,000$, $r = 12\%$ compounded annually, and $N = 6$ semi-annuals

Find: P

Approach: This is rather an unusual situation—the payment period is more frequent than the compounding period. You still need to find out the effective interest rate for semi-annual period.

- Effective interest rate per semi-annual payment period:

$$0.12 = (1+i)^2 - 1$$
$$(1+i)^2 = 1.12$$
$$i = 5.8301\% \text{ per semi-annual}$$

- Equivalence calculation:

$$N = 3 \times 2 = 6 \text{ years}$$
$$P = \$1,000(P/A,5.8301\%,6)$$
$$= \$4,943.68$$

3s.10 At what rate of interest, compounded quarterly, will an investment double itself in 5 years?

(a) 14.87%   (b) 3.72%

(c) 3.53%   (d) 14.11%.

Solution:

Given: $F = 2P$ and $N = 20$ quarters

Find: i

$$F = P(F/P, i, 20)$$
$$2P = P(1+i)^{20}$$
$$(1+i)^{20} = 2$$
$$i = 3.5265\%$$

3s.11 A series of equal quarterly deposits of $1000 extends over a period of 3 years. What is the future worth of this quarterly deposit series at 9% interest, compounded monthly?

(a) $13,160   (b) $12,590

(c) $13,615   (d) $13,112.

Solution:

Given: $A = \$1,000$, $r = 9\%$ compounded monthly, and $N = 12$ quarters

Find: F

Approach: Since the payment period is "quarterly," we need to find out the effective interest rate per quarter.

$$i = (1 + 0.09/12)^3 - 1 = 2.267\% \text{ per quarter}$$
$$F = \$1,000(F/A, 2.267\%, 12)$$
$$= \$13,615.27$$

3s.12 A series of equal quarterly receipts of $1000 extends over a period of 5 years. What is the present worth of this quarterly payment series at 8% interest, compounded *continuously*?

(a) $16,351   (b) $16,320

(c) $15,971   (d) $18,345.

Solution:

Given: $A = \$1,000$, $r = 8\%$ compounded continuously, and $N = 20$ quarters

26

Find: P

Approach: You need to find out the effective interest rate per quarter. Note that the compounding scheme is continuous, so the correct formula to use is $i = e^{r/K} - 1$, where $r = 8\%$ and $K = 4$.

$$i = e^{0.08/4} - 1 = 2.02\% \text{ per quarter}$$
$$P = \$1,000(P/A, 2.02\%, 20)$$
$$= \$16,320$$

3s.13 How many years will it take for an investment to double itself if the interest rate is 9%, compounded quarterly?

(a) $7 < N = 8$ years
(b) $8 < N = 9$ years
(c) $9 < N = 10$ years
(d) $10 < N = 11$ years.

Solution:

Given: $F = 2P$ and $r = 9\%$ compounded quarterly
Find: N

$$i_a = (1 + 0.09/4)^4 - 1 = 9.3083\% \text{ per year}$$
$$2 = 1(F/P, 9.3083\%, N)$$
$$N = 8 \text{ years}$$

3s.14 Suppose you deposit $\$C$ at the end of each month for 10 years at an interest rate of 12%, compounded continuously. What equal end-of-year deposit over 10 years would accumulate the same amount at the end of 10 years under the same interest compounding?

(a) $A = [12C(F/A, 12.75\%, 10)] \times (A/F, 12.75\%, 10)$
(b) $A = C(F/A, 1.005\%, 12)$
(c) $A = [C(F/A, 1\%, 120)] \times (A/F, 12\%, 10)$
(d) $A = C(F/A, 1.005\%, 120) \times (A/F, 12.68\%, 10)$
(e) None of the above.

Solution:

Given: $A = \$C$, $r = 12\%$ compounded annually, and $N = 120$ months

Find: Equivalent end-of-year deposit (A)

Approach: Basically we are looking for one lump sum end-of-year payment that is equivalent to 12 monthly payments of C. Since the payment period is monthly, we need to find the effective interest rate per month, which is $i = e^{0.12/12} - 1 = 1.005\%$ per month. The answer, is (b).

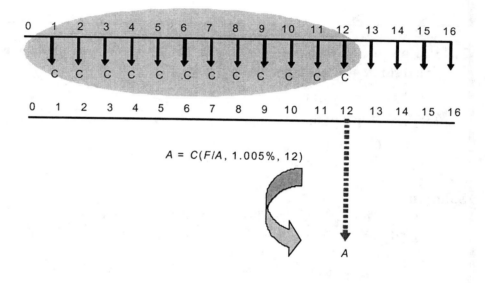

$$A = C(F/A, 1.005\%, 12)$$

3s.15 Compute the value of F, if the interest rate is 8%, compounded quarterly.

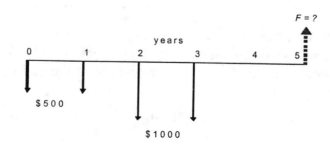

(a) $3,840

(b) $3,870

(c) $3,900

(d) $3,930

Solution:

> Given: $A = \$1,000$, $r = 8\%$ compounded quarterly, and $N = 5$ years
>
> Find: F
>
> Approach: Since the payment period is annual, you need to find out the effective annual interest rate, which is $i = (1 + 0.08/4)^4 - 1 = 8.2432\%$.
>
> $$F = \$500(F/P, 8.2432\%, 5) + \$500(F/P, 8.2432\%, 4)$$
> $$+\$1,000(F/P, 8.2432\%, 3) + \$1,000(F/P, 8.2432\%, 2)$$
> $$= \$3,869.20$$

3s.16 Henry Jones is planning to retire in 15 years. He wishes to deposit an equal amount (A) every 6 months until he retires so that, beginning one year following his retirement, he will receive annual payments of $30,000 for the next 15 years. Determine the value of A which he should deposit every 6 months if the interest rate is 8%, compounded semi-annually.

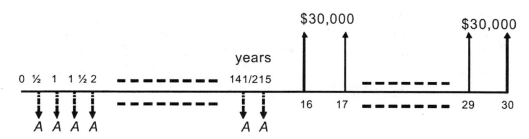

(a) $2,138

(c) $4,534

(b) $3,249

(d) $5,891

Solution:

> Given: annual withdrawal = $30,000, $r = 8\%$ compounded semi-annually, and $N = 30$ semi-annuals
>
> Find: A
>
> Approach: Set the base period at $n = 15$, then compute the equivalent total withdrawal and the equivalent total deposits at that period. For the equivalent withdrawal computation, the payment period is annual, so the effective annual interest rate should be calculated.
>
> - Equivalent total deposits at end of period 15:

$$V_{15} = A(F/A, 4\%, 30)$$
$$= 56.0849\,A$$

- Equivalent total withdrawals at end of period 15:

$$i_a = (1+0.08/2)^2 - 1 = 8.16\% \text{ per year}$$
$$P = \$30,000(P/A, 8.16\%, 15)$$
$$= \$254,295$$

- Required semiannual deposits (A):

$$V_{15} = P$$
$$56.0849\,A = \$254,295$$
$$A = \$4,534.10$$

3s.17 Suppose you deposit \$1,000 at the end of each quarter for 5 years at an interest of 8% compounded continuously. What equal end-of-year deposit over 5 years would accumulate the same amount at the end of 5 years under the same interest compounding (8%, compounded continuously)? To answer the question, which of the following is *correct*?

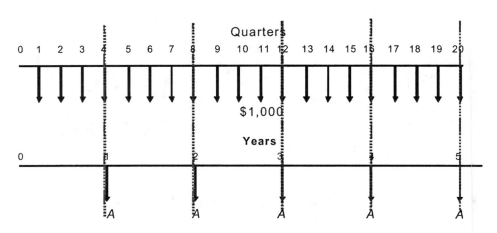

(a) $A = \$1,000 \times (F/A, 2\%, 20) \times (A/F, 8\%, 5)$

(b) $A = \$1,000 \times (F/A, e^{0.02} - 1, 4)$

(c) $A = \$1,000 \times (F/A, e^{0.02} - 1, 20) \times (A/F, 8\%, 5)$

(d) None of the above

30

Solution:

<u>Given</u>: deposit frequency = $1,000 per quarter, $r = 8$ compounded continuously, and $N = 20$ quarters

<u>Find</u>: Equivalent annual deposit amount (A)

<u>Approach</u>: What we are looking for is the amount of lump sum that is required at the end of each year. In other words, what is the single lump sum equivalent to 4 quarterly payments of $1,000?

$$i = e^{r/K} - 1$$
$$= e^{0.08/4} - 1$$
$$= 2.02\% \text{ per quarter}$$
$$A = \$1,000(F/A, 2.02\%, 4)$$
$$= \$4,122.84$$

The correct answer is (b).

3s.18 Assume you deposited $10,000 in a savings account that pays 6%, compounded monthly interest. You wish to withdraw $200 at the end of each month. How many months will it take to deplete the balance?

(a) $N < 48$ months
(b) $49 < N < 52$ months
(c) $53 < N < 56$ months
(d) $57 < N < 60$ months.

Solution:

<u>Given</u>: $P = \$10,000$, $r = 6\%$ compounded monthly, $A = \$200$ per month,
<u>Find</u>: N

$$\$200 = \$10,000(A/P, \frac{6\%}{12}, N)$$
$$N = 51 \text{ months}$$

3s.19 Find the value of P.

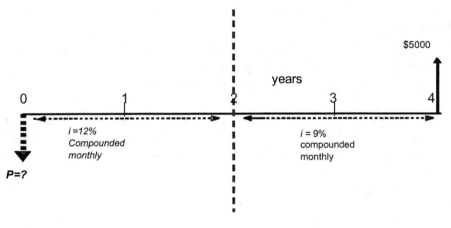

(a) $2,965   (c) $3,110
(b) $3,355   (d) $3,292

Solution:

Given: $F = \$5,000$, $r =$ changing interest rates, and $N = 5$ years
Find: P
Approach: With changing interest rates, we can calculate the equivalent present value in two steps. First, find the equivalent value of $5,000 ($V_2$) at $n = 2$ using $i_a = 9.38\%$, and then discount the value (V_2) again at $i_a = 12.68\%$.

$$V_2 = \$5,000(P/F,9.38\%,2)$$
$$= \$4,179.21$$
$$P = V_2(P/F,12.68\%,2)$$
$$= \$4,179.21(P/F,12.68\%,2)$$
$$= \$3,291.55$$

3s.20 You are considering purchasing a piece of industrial equipment that costs $30,000. You decide to make a down payment in the amount of $5,000 and to borrow the remainder from a local bank at an interest rate of 9%, compounded monthly. The loan is to be paid off in 36 monthly installments. What is the amount of the monthly payment?

(a) $954   (b) $833
(c) $795   (d) $694.

Solution:

Given: $P = \$25,000$, $r = 9\%$ compounded monthly, and $N = 36$ months

32

Find: A

$$i = \frac{9\%}{12} = 0.75\% \text{ per month}$$
$$A = \$25,000(A/P,0.75\%,36)$$
$$= \$795 \text{ per month}$$

3s.21 Vi Wilson is interested in buying an automobile priced at $18,000. From her personal savings, she can come up with a down payment in the amount of $3,000. The remaining balance will be financed by the dealer over a period of 36 months at an interest rate of 6.25%, compounded monthly. Which of the following statements is correct?

(a) The dealer's annual percentage rate (APR) is 6.432%.

(b) The monthly payment can be calculated by using $A = \$15,000(A/P, 6.25\%, 3)/12$.

(c) The monthly payment can be calculated by using $A = \$15,000(A/P, 0.5208\%, 36)$.

(d) The monthly payment can be calculated by using $A = \$15,000(A/P, 6.432\%/12, 3)$.

Solution:

Given: $P = \$18,000 - \$3,000 = \$15,000$, $r = 6.25\%$ compounded monthly, and $N = 36$ months

Find: A

$$i = \frac{6.25\%}{12} = 0.5208\% \text{ per month}$$
$$A = \$15,000(A/P,0.5208\%,36)$$
$$= \$584.66 \text{ per month}$$

The correct answer is (c).

3s.22 John secured a home improvement loan from a local bank in the amount of $10,000 at an interest rate of 9%, compounded monthly. He agreed to pay back the loan in 60 equal monthly installments. Immediately after the 24th payment, John decides to pay off the remainder of the loan in a lump sum. What will be the size of this payment?

(a) $P = \$7,473$ (b) $P = \$6,000$

(c) $P = \$6,528$ (d) $P = \$7,710$.

Solution:

Given: $P = \$10,000$, $r = 9\%$ compounded monthly, and $N = 60$ months
Find: lump sum amount to pay off the loan right after the 24th payment (B_{24})

Approach: First, we need to determine the monthly payment (A). After the 24th payment, there are still 36 monthly payments outstanding. From the bank's point of view, they are looking for a lump sum amount that is equivalent to these 36 future payments.

$$i = \frac{9\%}{12} = 0.75\% \text{ per month}$$

$$A = \$10,000(A/P, 0.75\%, 60)$$

$$= \$207.58 \text{ per month}$$

$$B_{24} = \$207.58(P/A, 0.75\%, 36)$$

$$= \$6,527.72$$

3s.23 You obtained a loan of $20,000 to finance the purchase of an automobile. Based on monthly compounding for 24 months, the end-of-the-month equal payment was figured out to be $922.90. Immediately after making the 12th payment, you decide you want to pay off the loan in lump sum. The size of this lump sum amount is nearest to which of the following?

(a) $10,498   (b) $11,075
(c) $12,044   (d) $12,546.

Solution:

Given: $P = \$20,000$, $A = \$922.90$, and $N = 24$ months
Find: B_{12}

Approach: This problem is similar to 3s.22, except that we do not know the interest rate used in calculating the monthly payment. Therefore, the first task is to determine the loan interest rate. Once this loan rate is known, the procedure will be exactly the same as 3s.22.

$$\$922.90 = \$20,000(A/P,i,24)$$
$$i = 0.8333\% \text{ per month}$$
$$B_{12} = \$922.90(P/A,0.8333\%,12)$$
$$= \$10,497.55$$

Comments: In finding the unknown interest rate, we may use the Excel's financial command, =RATE(24,922.90,-20,000).

3s.24 You borrowed $1,000 at 8%, compounded annually. The loan was repaid according to the following schedule.

n	Repayment Amount
1	$100
2	$300
3	$500
4	X

Find X, the amount that is required to pay off the loan at the end of year 4.

(a) $108   (b) $298
(c) $345   (d) $460.

Solution:

Given: $B = \$1,000$, payment series, $r = 8\%$ compounded annually, and $N = 4$ years
Find: X

$$\$1,000 = \$100(P/F,8\%,1) + \$300(P/F,8\%,2)$$
$$+ \$500(P/F,8\%,3) + X(P/F,8\%,4)$$
$$\$1,000 = \$746.71 + 0.7350X$$
$$X = \$344.60$$

3s.25 Compute the lump sum amount required at the end of year 4 to repay an amount of $20,000 borrowed today at an interest rate of 12%, compounded monthly.

(a) $20,812   (c) $31,470

(b) $27,812   (d) $32,244

Solution:

Given: $P = \$20,000$, $r = 12\%$ compounded monthly, and $N = 48$ months
Find: F

$$F = \$20,000(F/P,1\%,48)$$
$$= \$32,244$$

3s.26 Suppose you borrowed $10,000 at an interest rate of 12%, compounded monthly over 36 months. At the end of the first year (after 12 payments), you want to negotiate with the bank to pay off the remainder of the loan in 8 equal quarterly payments. What is the amount of this quarterly payment, if the interest rate and compounding frequency remain the same?

(a) $875   (c) $996
(b) $925   (d) $1,006

Solution:

Given: $P = \$10,000$, $r = 12\%$ compounded monthly, and $N = 36$ months
Find: Required quarterly payments

Approach: First determine the required monthly payment for the original loan. Then, calculate the required lump sum payment after the 12th payment. Finally, spread this lump sum amount over 8 quarters.

- Monthly payment:

$$A = \$10,000(A/P,1\%,36)$$
$$= \$332.14$$

- Loan balance right after the 12th payment:

$$B_{12} = \$332.14(P/A,1\%,24)$$
$$= \$7,055.77$$

- Quarterly payment:

$$i = (1+0.12/12)^3 - 1$$
$$= 3.03\% \text{ per quarter}$$
$$C = \$7,055.77(A/P, 3.03\%, 8)$$
$$= \$1,006.41 \text{ per quarter}$$

Chapter 4 Equivalence Calculations under Inflation

4s.1 The following figures represent the CPI indices (base period 1982–1984 = 100) for urban consumers in U.S. cities. Determine the average general inflation rate between 1998 and 2002. Use the following data:

Base	Calendar Year	CPI
0	1998	163.0
1	1999	166.6
2	2000	172.2
3	2001	177.1
4	2002	179.9

The average inflation rate between 1998 and 2002 is

(a) 1.99%   (b) 2.50%

(c) 3.05%   (d) 3.64%.

Solution:

Given: CPI data, $N = 4$, $CPI_0 = 163.0$, $CPI_4 = 179.9$

Find: general inflation rate ($\bar{f}$)

Approach:

$$CPI_n = CPI_0(1+\bar{f})^n$$

$$\bar{f} = \left[\frac{CPI_n}{CPI_0}\right]^{1/n} - 1$$

$$= \left[\frac{179.9}{163.0}\right]^{1/4} - 1$$

$$= 2.4969\%$$

4s.2 How many years will it take for the dollar's purchasing power to be one-half what it is now, if the average inflation rate is expected to continue at the rate of 9% for an indefinite period? (Hint: You may apply the Rule of 72.)

(a) About 6 years   (b) About 8 years

(c) About 10 years (d) About 12 years.

Solution:

Given: $f = 9\%$,

Find: the number of years (N) it takes to reduce the dollar's purchasing power to be one-half

Approach: The Rule of 72 can determine approximately how long it will take for a sum of money to "double." The rule states that, to find the time it takes for the present value, of money to grow by a factor of 2, we divide 72 by the interest rate. The same rule can be applied to any inflation situation. In other words, if the purchasing power is reduced by one-half, it will cost twice of the amount to purchase the same quantity of goods or services.

- Using the Exact formula:

$$2 = 1(1 + 0.09)^N$$
$$\ln 2 = N \ln 1.09$$
$$N = \frac{\ln 2}{\ln 1.09}$$
$$= 8.0417 \text{ years}$$

- Using the Rule of 72:

$$N \cong \frac{72}{9} = 8 \text{ years}$$

4s.3 Suppose you have experienced inflation for the past 2 years as follows: the first year's inflation rate is 5%, and the second year year's rate is 8%. Calculate the average inflation rate for a 2-year period.

(a) 3%　　　　　　　(b) 6.49%

(c) 6.5%　　　　　　(d) 13%.

Solution:

Given: periodic inflation rates (5% for the first year, 8% for the second year), $N = 2$

Find: f

$$(1 + 0.05)(1 + 0.08) = 1.134$$
$$(1 + f)^2 = 1.134$$
$$f = 6.4894\%$$

4s.4   Assume the expected inflation rate to be 3%. If the current inflation-free interest rate is 4%, what ought the market interest rate to be?

(a) 7%   (b) 12%

(c) 1%   (d) 7.12%.

Solution:

Given: $f = 3\%$, $i' = 4\%$

Find: i

$$i = i' + f + i' f$$
$$= 0.04 + 0.03 + (0.04)(0.03)$$
$$= 0.0712 \text{ (or } 7.12\%)$$

4s.5   A series of five constant-dollar (or real-dollar) payments, beginning with $6,000 at the end of the first year, are increasing at the rate of 5% per year. Assume that the average general inflation rate is 4%, and the market interest rate is 11% during this inflationary period. What is the equivalent present worth of the series?

(a) $24,259   (b) $25,892

(c) $27,211   (d) $29,406.

Solution:

Given: a geometric cash flow series with $A_1 = \$6,000$ and $g = 5\%$, $i = 11\%$, and $\overline{f} = 4\%$

Find: P

Approach: Since the cash flow series are given in constant dollars, you should use an inflation-free interest rate (i') to find the present value.

$$i = i' + f + i'f$$

$$i' = \frac{i - \overline{f}}{1 + \overline{f}} = \frac{0.11 - 0.04}{1.04}$$

$$= 6.73\%$$

$$P = A_1 \left[\frac{1 - (1 + g)^N (1 + i')^{-N}}{i' - g} \right]$$

$$= \$6,000 \left[\frac{1 - (1 + 0.05)^5 (1 + 0.0673)^{-5}}{0.0673 - 0.05} \right]$$

$$= \$6,000(4.5353)$$

$$= \$27,211.73$$

4s.6 "At a market interest rate of 7% per year and an inflation rate of 5% per year, a series of three equal annual receipts of $100 in constant dollars is equivalent to a series of three annual receipts of $105 in actual dollars." Which of the following statements is correct?

(a) The amount of actual dollars is overstated.

(b) The amount of actual dollars is understated.

(c) The amount of actual dollars is about right.

(d) Sufficient information is not available to make a comparison.

Solution:

Given: $i = 7\%$, $\overline{f} = 5\%$, $A' = \$100$, $A = \$105$, $N = 3$ years

Find: present value for each cash flow series

Approach: To compare two different cash flow series (one series given in constant dollars, and the other series in actual dollars), we need to identify the market interest rate as well as the inflation-free interest rate. For a cash flow series given in constant dollars, we use the inflation-free interest rate to find the equivalent present value. For a cash flow series given in actual dollars, we use the market interest rate to find the equivalent present value of the series.

$$i = i' + f + i'f$$

$$i' = \frac{i - \overline{f}}{1 + \overline{f}} = \frac{0.07 - 0.05}{1.05}$$

$$= 1.9\%$$

41

- Constant dollar series:

$$P_1 = \$100(P/A, 1.9\%, 3)$$
$$= \$288.95$$

- Actual dollar series:

$$P_2 = \$105(P/A, 7\%, 3)$$
$$= \$275.55$$

The amount of actual dollars is understated by $13.39, so the correct answer is (b).

4s.7 Which of the following statements is *incorrect*?

   (a) A negative inflation rate implies that you are experiencing a deflationary economy.

   (b) Under an inflationary economy, debt financing is always a preferred option because you are paying back with cheaper dollars.

   (c) Bond interest rates will tend to be higher in the financial market, so that it would cost more to finance a new project.

   (d) A general inflation rate is calculated based on the consumer price index.

Solution:

Given: statements above

Find: which statement is incorrect?

- Statement (a) is correct.
- Statement (b) is not necessary correct, as lenders will raise the borrowing interest rates to compensate the loss from purchasing power under inflationary environment.
- Statement (c) is correct.
- Statement (d) is correct.

4s.8 Suppose that you borrow $20,000 at 12%, compounded monthly, over 5 years. Knowing that the 12% represents the market interest rate, the monthly payment in actual dollars will be $444.90. If the average monthly general inflation rate is expected to be 0.5%, what is the equivalent equal monthly payment series in constant dollars?

(a) $386   (b) $445
(c) $486   (d) $345.

Solution:

Given: $P = \$20,000$, $i = 12\%$ compounded monthly (or 1% per month), $\bar{f} = 0.5\%$ per month, $N = 60$ months, $A = \$444.90$ per month

Find: A'

Approach: First determine the inflation-free interest rate (i'). Then calculate the monthly payment in constant dollars (A') using this inflation-free interest rate. Since the payment period is monthly, you need to express all (i', i, and $\bar{f}$) on monthly basis.

$$i = i' + \bar{f} + i'\bar{f}$$

$$i' = \frac{i - \bar{f}}{1 + \bar{f}} = \frac{0.01 - 0.005}{1.005}$$

$$= 0.4975\% \text{ per month}$$

$$A' = \$20,000(P/A, 0.4975\%, 60)$$

$$= \$386.38$$

4s.9 A proposed project that requires an investment of $10,000 (now) is expected to generate a series of five equal payments ($6,000 each in constant dollars). Assume that the average inflation rate is 4%, and the market interest rate (i) is 10% during this inflationary period. What is the equivalent present worth of this investment?

(a) $15,434   (b) $15,274
(c) $12,745   (d) $16,711.

Solution:

Given: $I = \$10,000$, $A' = \$6,000$, $\bar{f} = 4\%$, $i = 10\%$, $N = 5$

Find: P

$$i = i' + f + i'f$$

$$i' = \frac{i - \bar{f}}{1 + \bar{f}} = \frac{0.10 - 0.04}{1.04}$$

$$= 5.7692\%$$

$$P = -\$10,000 + \$6,000(P/A, 5.7692\%, 5)$$

$$= \$15,433.64$$

4s.10 A father wants to save in advance for his 8-year old daughter's college expenses. The daughter will enter the college 10 years from now. An annual amount of $20,000 in today's dollars (constant dollars) will be required to support the college for 4 years. Assume that these college payments will be made at the *beginning* of each school year. (The first payment occurs at the end of 10 years). The future general inflation rate is estimated to be 5% per year, and the interest rate on the savings account will be 8% compounded quarterly (market interest rate) during this period. If the father has decided to save only $1,000 (actual dollars) each quarter, how much will the daughter have to borrow to cover her sophomore expenses?

(a) $4,120   (b) $4,314

(c) $4,000   (d) $4,090.

Solution:

Given: i = 8% compounded quarterly (or 2% per quarter), $\bar{f}$ = 5%, A = $1,000 per quarter, N = 10 years (40 quarters), required college expenses ($20,000 in today's dollars)

Find: the amount that needs to be borrowed in sophomore

Approach: Since some of the cash flow elements are estimated in constant dollars, and others are estimated in actual dollars, it is important to convert all cash flows into one type (in this case, actual dollars). First task is to estimate the future college expenses in actual dollars. Then determine the total amount accumulated in the savings account at the end of 10 years. From this, the first-year college expenses will be paid out. The remaining balance will continue to earn 2% interest each quarter until the sophomore year. If the resulting balance at the beginning of the sophomore year is less than the required college expenses at that time, the difference must be borrowed.

- Required college expenses in actual dollars:

    1st year: $20,000(P/F, 5% 10) = \$32,577.89
    2nd year: $20,000(F/P, 5%, 11) = \$34,206.28
    3rd year: $20,000(F/P, 5%, 12) = \$35,917.13
    4th year: $20,000(F/P, 5%, 13) = \$37,712.98

- Amount saved at the end of 10 years:

$$V_{10} = \$1,000(F/A, 2\%, 40) = \$60,401.98$$

- Required borrowing at the beginning of sophomore year:

    o Balance right after the first year payment:

$$B_{10} = \$60,401.98 - \$32,577.89$$
$$= \$27,824.09$$

    o Balance right after the 2nd year payment:

$$B_{11} = \$27,824.09(F/P, 2\%, 4) - \$34,206.28$$
$$= \$30,117.68 - \$34,206.28$$
$$= \$4,088.59$$

Chapter 5 Present-Worth Analysis

5s.1 An investment project costs P. It is expected to have an annual net cash flow of $0.125P$ for 20 years. What is the project's payback period?

(a) 8 years

(b) 0 year

(c) 6 years

(d) 11 years

Solution:

> Given: investment and cash flows, $N = 20$ years
> Find: conventional payback period
> Approach:

$$\text{Payback period} = \frac{P}{0.125P} = 8 \text{ years}$$

5s.2 Which of the following statements is incorrect?

(a) If two investors are considering the same project, the payback period will be longer for the investor with the higher MARR.

(b) If you were to consider the cost of funds in a payback period calculation, you would have to wait longer to breakeven as you increase the interest rate.

(c) Considering the cost of funds in a payback calculation is equivalent to finding the time period when the project balance becomes zero.

(d) The simplicity of the payback period method is one of its most appealing qualities even though it fails to measure project profitability.

Solution:

> Given: information regarding payback periods
> Find: conceptually correct statement
> - Statement (a): It is *only true* when you consider the cost of funds in calculating the payback period, known as "discounted payback period." For a conventional payback period, the cost of funds is not factored into the calculations.
> - Statement (b): This is a correct statement. At a higher interest rate, the cost of funds also increases, which delays the recovery of the investment.
> - Statement (c): This is also a correct statement. The project balance being zero means that the investor recovers all the investments made

in the project as well as the cost of funds (opportunity cost) incurred up to that point.

- Statement (d): It is a correct statement. The computational simplicity makes the method popular among practitioners.

The correct answer is (a).

5s.3 Find the net present worth of the following cash flow series at an interest rate of 10%.

End of Period	Cash Flow
0	-$100
1	-200
2	300
3	400
4	500

   (a) $500 < PW(10\%) = \$550$
   (b) $\$550 < PW(10\%) = \$600$
   (c) $\$600 < PW(10\%) = \$650$
   (d) $\$650 < PW(10\%) = \$700.$

Solution:
     Given: cash flow series, MARR = 10%
     Find: PW(10%)

$$PW(10\%) = -\$100 - \$200(P/F,10\%,1) + \$300(P/F,10\%,2)$$
$$+ \$400(P/F,10\%,3) + \$500(P/F,10\%,4)$$
$$= \$608.14$$

5s.4 You are considering buying an old house that you will convert into an office building for rental. Assuming that you will own the property for 10 years, how much would you be willing to pay for the old house now given the following financial data?

- Remodeling cost at period 0 = $20,000
- Annual rental income = $25,000
- Annual upkeep costs (including taxes) = $5,000

47

- Estimated net property value (after taxes) at the end of 10 years?= $225,000

- The time value of your money (interest rate)?= 8% per year.

(a) $201,205   (b) $218,420

(c) $232,316   (d) $250,100.

Solution:

> Given: financial data, MARR = 8%, $N = 10$ years
> Find: P
> Approach: To figure out the value of the property, you can discount all future benefits less any expenses. If you pay more than these discounted net benefits, you are losing money on the investment.

$$PW(8\%) = -\$20,000 + (\$25,000 - \$5,000)(P/A,8\%,10)$$
$$+\$225,000(P/F,8\%,10)$$
$$= \$218,420$$

5s.5 Your R&D group has developed and tested a computer software package that assists engineers to control the proper chemical mix for the various process-manufacturing industries. If you decide to market the software, your first year operating net cash flow is estimated to be $1,000,000. Because of market competition, product life will be about 4 years, and the product's market share will decrease by 25% each year over the previous year's share. You are approached by a big software house which wants to purchase the right to manufacture and distribute the product. Assuming that your interest rate is 15%, for what minimum price would you be willing to sell the software?

(a) $2,507,621   (b) $2,887,776

(c) $2,766,344   (d) $2,047,734.

Solution:

> Given: financial data above, $N = 4$ years, MARR = 15%
> Find: minimum selling price
> Approach: This problem is similar to 5s.4 in that the discounted net future benefits are the basis to setting the starting price.

$$PW(15\%) = \$1,000,000\left[\frac{1-(1-0.25)^4(1+0.15)^{-4}}{0.15-(-0.25)}\right]$$

$$= \$1,000,000(2.047734)$$

$$= \$2,047,734$$

Comments: Of course, there is no way of knowing that the buyer will pay this price, but you need to do your own homework before sitting at the negotiating table. In other words, you have to know where you stand when the buyer offers to buy your asset.

5s.6 Which of the following investment options would maximize your future wealth at the end of 5 years if you plan to invest $500 today?

(a) 12%, compounded annually

(b) 11.75%, compounded semiannually

(c) 11.5%, compounded quarterly

(d) 11.25%, compounded monthly

Solution:

Given: $I = \$500$, $N = 5$ years

Find: the best interest earning opportunity

Approach: As we learned in Chapter 3, when we compare different interest earning opportunities, we need to compare them on an effective annual basis.

$(a)\ i_a = 12\%$

$(b)\ i_a = (1+0.1175/2)^2 - 1 = 12.095\%$

$(c)\ i_a = (1+0.1150/4)^4 - 1 = 12.006\%$

$(d)\ i_a = (1+0.1125/12)^{12} - 1 = 11.8486\%$

The correct answer is (b), as the annual effective interest is the largest.

5s.7 What is the capitalized equivalent amount, at 10% annual interest, for a series of annual receipts of $400 for the first 10 years, which will increase to $500 per year after 10 years, and which will remain constant thereafter?

(a) $4,621   (b) $4,386

(c) $4,452   (d) $9,854.

Solution:

Given: cash flow series in perpetuity, MARR = 10%

Find: capitalized equivalent worth

Approach: The original cash flow series can be divided into two series: the first one is the $400 series in perpetuity and the second one is the $100 series in perpetuity starting after 10 years.

$$CE(10\%) = \frac{\$400}{0.10} + \frac{\$100}{0.10}(P/F,10\%,10)$$
$$= \$4,000 + \$386$$
$$= \$4,386$$

5s.8 Find the capitalized equivalent worth for the project cash flow series at an interest rate of 10%.

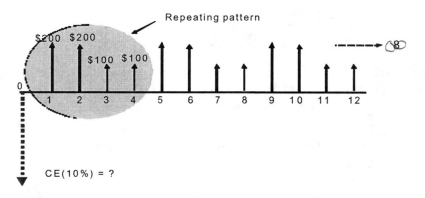

(a) $CE(10\%) = \$1,476$

(b) $CE(10\%) = \$1,548$

(c) $CE(10\%) = \$1,500$

(d) $CE(10\%) = \$1,753$.

Solution:

Given: cash flow series, MARR = 10%, $N = 8$

Find: capitalized equivalent worth

Approach: Since there are repeating patterns over time, our task is to convert the cash flow series within the pattern into the equivalent annual values. This is equivalent to finding the equivalent annual values over the entire series.

$$PW(10\%)_{\text{first cycle}} = \$100(P/A,10\%,4) + \$100(P/A,10\%,2)$$
$$= \$490.54$$
$$AE(10\%) = \$490.54(A/P,10\%,4)$$
$$= \$154.75$$
$$CE(10\%) = \frac{\$154.75}{0.10}$$
$$= \$1547.50$$

5s.9 The following table contains a summary of how a project's balance is expected to change over its 5-year service life at 10% interest.

End of Period	Project Balance
0	-$1,000
1	-1,500
2	600
3	900
4	1,500
5	2,000

Which of the following statements is incorrect?

(a) The required additional investment at the end of period 1 is $500.

(b) The net present worth of the project at 10% interest is $1,242.

(c) The net future of the project at 10% interest is $2,000.

(d) Within 2 years, the company will recover all its investments and the cost of funds (interest) from the project.

Solution:

Given: project balances over the life of the project, $N = 5$, and MARR = 10%

Find: incorrect statement

Approach:

- Statement (a): Since $PB(10\%)_0 = -\$1,000$ and $PB(10\%)_1 = -\$1,500$, we can figure out what the cash flow at period 1 is.

$$PB(10\%)_1 = PB(10\%)_0(1+0.10) + A_1$$
$$= -\$1,500$$
$$-\$1,000(1.1) + A_1 = -\$1,500$$
$$A_1 = -\$400$$

- Statement (b): Since the net future worth is the terminal project balance, we find the net present value as follows:

$$PB(10\%)_5 = FW(10\%)$$
$$= \$2,000$$
$$PW(10\%) = \$2,000(P/F,10\%,5)$$
$$= \$1,241.84$$

- Statement (c) is correct.
- Statement (d): Since $PB(10\%)_2 = \$600 > 0$, we can say that the initial investment as well as the cost of funds were fully recovered and there are \$600 surplus at the end of period 2.

The correct answer is (a).

5s.10 Reconsider the project balance table calculated at 10% given in 5s.9.

End of Period	Project Balance
0	-$1,000
1	-$1,500
2	$600
3	$900
4	$1,500
5	$2,000

Which of the following statements is *correct?*

(a) The project is not profitable at $i = 10\%$.
(b) The conventional payback period is 1.7 years.
(c) The cash flow in period 3 is $240.
(d) The Net Present Worth of the project is $2,000.

Solution:

<u>Given</u>: project balances at 10%
<u>Find</u>: the correct statement

- Statement (a): incorrect – Note that the terminal project balance $(PB(10\%)_5 = \$2,000)$ is the net future worth of the project. Since $PB(10\%)_5 = FW(10\%) > 0$, $PW(10\%)$ should be also positive.
- Statement (b): incorrect—The conventional payback period is based on undiscounted cash flows. The discounted payback period is based on project balances, which is 1.7 years.
- Statement (c): correct – Based on $PB(10\%)_2$ and $PB(10\%)_3$, we can find the cash flow at period 3 (A_3) as follows:

$$PB(10\%)_3 = PB(10\%)_2(1+0.10) + A_3$$

$$\$900 = \$600(1.1) + A_3$$

$$A_3 = \$240$$

- Statement (d): incorrect—The net future worth is $2,000, so $PW(10\%)$ should be less than $2,000.

5s.11 NasTech Corporation purchased a vibratory finishing machine for $20,000 in year 0. The useful life of the machine is 10 years, at the end of which, the machine is estimated to have a zero salvage value. The machine generates net annual revenues of $6,000. The annual operating and maintenance expenses are estimated to be $1,000. If NasTech's MARR is 15%, how many years does it take before this machine becomes profitable?

(a)   3 years $< n = 4$ years

(b)   4 years $< n = 5$ years

(c)   5 years $< n = 6$ years

(d)   6 years $< n = 7$ years

Solution:

Given: $I = \$20,000$, $N = 10$ years, $S = \$0$, Net annual cash flow $(A_n) = \$5,000$, MARR = 15%

Find: the number years to operate to become profitable

$$PW(15\%) = -\$20,000 + \$5,000(P/A, 15\%, N)$$

$$= 0$$

$$(P/A, 15\%, N) = 4$$

$$N = 6.5561$$

Comments: The question is equivalent to finding the discounted payback period, or looking for N that makes $PB(15\%)_n = 0$.

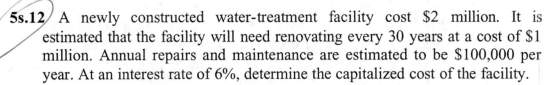

5s.12 A newly constructed water-treatment facility cost $2 million. It is estimated that the facility will need renovating every 30 years at a cost of $1 million. Annual repairs and maintenance are estimated to be $100,000 per year. At an interest rate of 6%, determine the capitalized cost of the facility.

(a) $3,360,343   (b) $3,579,806

(c) $3,877,482   (d) $4,301,205

Solution:

Given: $I = \$2,000,000$, $i = 6\%$, $N = 8$, annual repair & maintenance = $100,000, renovation cost = $1,000,000 every 30 years

Find: capitalized cost of the facility

Approach: The equivalent construction cost as well as repair & maintenance costs can be calculated easily. However, the renovation costs occur every 30 years. We need to find the equivalent annual renovation cost by using the factor $(F/A, 6\%, 30)$. Then divide this annual value by 6% to determine the portion of the capitalized cost from renovation.

- Construction cost (P_1):
$$P_1 = \$2,000,000$$

- Repair and maintenance cost (P_2):

$$P_2 = \frac{\$100,000}{0.06} = \$1,666,667$$

- Renovation cost (P_3):

$$P_3 = \frac{\$1,000,000(A/F,6\%,30)}{0.06}$$

$$= \frac{\$12,649}{0.06}$$

$$= \$210,815$$

- Total cost (P):

$$P = P_1 + P_2 + P_3$$

$$= \$3,877,482$$

5s.13 Alpha Company is planning to invest in a machine, the use of which will result in the following:

- Annual revenues of $10,000 in the first year and increases of $5,000 each year, up to year 9. From year 10, the revenues will remain constant ($52,000) for an indefinite period.

- The machine is to be overhauled every 10 years. The expense for each overhaul is $40,000.

If Alpha expects a present worth of at least $100,000 at a MARR of 10% for this project, what is the maximum investment that Alpha should be prepared to make?

(a) $250,140   (b) $674,697

(c) $350,100   (d) $509,600

Solution:

Given: financial data given above, $N = 8$, MARR $= 10\%$, $PW(10\%) = \$100,000$

Find: required investment to make the project breakeven

Approach:

- Required investment (P_1):
- Equivalent revenue streams (P_2):

$$P_2 = \$10,000(P/A,10\%,9) + \$5,000(P/G,10\%,9)$$
$$+ \frac{\$52,000}{0.10}(P/F,10\%,9)$$
$$= \$375,228$$

- Equivalent machine overhaul expenses (P_3):
$$P_3 = \frac{\$40,000(A/F,10\%,10)}{0.10}$$
$$= \frac{\$2,508}{0.10}$$
$$= \$25,080$$

- Required investment (P_1):

$$P = P_1 + P_2 + P_3$$
$$\$100,000 = P_1 + \$375,228 - \$25,080$$
$$P_1 = -\$250,148$$

5s.14 Consider the following two investment alternatives:

| | Net Cash Flow | |
End of Year	Machine A	Machine B
0	-$1,000	-$2,000
1	900	2,500
2	800	800 +200
3	700	

Suppose that your firm needs either machine for only 2 years. The net proceeds from the sale of machine B are estimated to be $200. What should be the required net proceeds from the sale of machine A so that both machines could be considered economically indifferent at an interest rate of 10%?

(a) $700   (b) $750

(c) $800   (d) $850.

Solution:

Given: cash flows for both projects, planning horizon (study period) = 2 years, MARR = 10%

Find: S, the net proceeds from the sale of machine A that makes two projects indifferent

Approach:

$$PW(10\%)_A = -\$1,000 + \$900(P/F,10\%,1)$$
$$+ (\$800 + S)(P/F,10\%,2)$$
$$= \$479.33 + 0.8264S$$
$$PW(10\%)_B = -\$2,000 + \$2,500(P/F,10\%,1)$$
$$+ (\$800 + \$200)(P/F,10\%,2)$$
$$= \$1,099.17$$

$$\text{Let } PW(10\%)_A = PW(10\%)_B$$
$$\$479.33 + 0.8264S = \$1,099.17$$
$$S = \$750$$

5s.15 Consider the following two mutually exclusive service projects with project lives of 3 years and 2 years, respectively. (The mutually exclusive service projects will have identical revenues for each year of service.) The interest rate is known to be 12%.

| End of Year | Net Cash Flow | |
	Project A	Project B
0	-$1,000	-$800
1	-400	-200
2	-400	-200 + 0
3	-400 + 200	

If the required service period is 6 years, and both projects can be repeated with the given costs and better service projects are unavailable in the future, which project is better and why? Choose from the following options:

(a) Select project B because it will save you $344 in present worth over the required service period.

(b) Select project A because it will cost $1,818 in NPW each cycle, with only one replacement, whereas project B will cost $1,138 in NPW each cycle, with two replacements.

(c) Select project B because its NPW exceeds that of project A by $680.

(d) None of the above.

Solution:

Given: cash flows, MARR = 12%, required service period = 6 years

Find: the correct statement

Approach: Since both projects can be repeated with the same cash flows, we may need to find out how many replacements should be made for each option. Clearly, one replacement is required for Project A, while two more replacements for Project B. Then, calculate the net present value for each replacement option over 6 years.

- Project A with one future replacement:

$$PW(12\%)_{A, \text{ first cycle}} = -\$1,000 - \$400(P/A,12\%,3) + \$200(P/F,12\%,3)$$

$$= -\$1,818.37$$

$$PW(12\%)_{A, \text{ over 6 years}} = -\$1,818.37[1 + (P/F,12\%,3)]$$

$$= -\$3,112.66$$

- Project B with two future replacements:

$$PW(12\%)_{\text{B, first cycle}} = -\$8,000 - \$200(P/A,12\%,2)$$
$$= -\$1,138.01$$
$$PW(12\%)_{\text{B, over 6 years}} = -\$1,138.01[1 + (P/F,12\%,2) + (P/F,12\%,4)]$$
$$= -\$2,768.45$$

The correct answer is (a).

5s.16 Gene Research, Inc. just finished a 4-year R&D and clinical trials successfully and expects a quick approval from the Food and Drug Administration. If the company markets the product on their own, it requires $30 million immediately ($n ⁼ 0$) to build a new manufacturing facility, and it is expected to have a 10 year product life. The R&D expenditure in the previous years and the anticipated revenues that the company can generate over the next 10 years is summarized as follows:

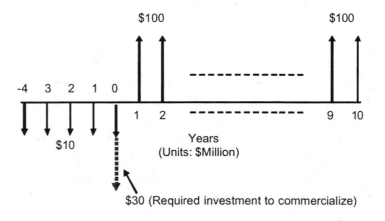

$30 (Required investment to commercialize)

Merck, a large drug company is interested in purchasing the R&D project and the right to commercialize the product from Gene Research, Inc., immediately ($n?=?0$). What would be a starting negotiating price for the project from Merck? Assume that Gene's MARR⁼ 20%.

(a) $105 million
(b) $420 million
(c) $494 million
(d) $524 million

Solution:
Given: financial data, MARR = 20%,

Find: right selling price
Approach:

- Anticipated future benefits:
$$V_{\text{future benefits}} = \$100(P/A,20\%,10)$$
$$= \$419.25$$

- Equivalent investment made in the project:
$$V_{\text{equ. investment}} = \$10(P/F,20\%,4) + \$10(F/P,20\%,4) + \$30$$
$$= \$104.42$$

Didn't understand

- Required selling price:

$$V = \$419.25 + \$104.42$$
$$= \$523.67$$

Comments: The absolute minimum asking price is $104.42, because that is how much you have invested in the project. However, if you go with this absolute minimum, you are giving up the future benefits that the R&D project would generate. Certainly, we have no way of knowing that Merck would pay this price, but it opens up the point of negotiation.

5s.17 A manufacturing company is considering the purchase of a new CNC lathe, which will cost $60,000 and has an annual maintenance cost of $8,000. A few parts in the lathe need to be replaced once every 5 years to enable smooth running of the lathe. This would cost an additional $20,000 (once every 5 years). Assuming that the lathe would last 15 years under these conditions, what is the total equivalent cost (present value) of this investment at an interest rate of 12%? (Assume that there will be no appreciable salvage value at the end of 15 years.)

(a) $114,487   (c) $135,928

(b) $132,275   (d) $72,275

Solution:

Given: $I = \$60,000$, O&M cost = $8,000 per year, replacement cost = $20,000 once every 5 years, $N = 15$ years, and MARR = 12%
Find: PW(12%)
Approach:

$$PW(12\%) = -\$60,000 - \$8,000(P/A,12\%,15)$$
$$-\$20,000\big[(P/F,12\%,5) + (P/F,12\%,10)\big]$$
$$= -\$132,275$$

Comments: Note that the replacement cost at the end of year 15 is not required as the equipment will be no longer in service after 15 years.

5s.18 A manufacturing company is considering two mutually exclusive machines E1 and E2 with the following cash flow information:

	Machine E1		Machine E2	
Year	Cash Flow	Salvage Value	Cash Flow	Salvage Value
0	-$400		-$600	
1	-$300	$200	-$250	$400
2	-$300	$175	-$250	$360
3	-$300	$150	-$250	$320
4			-$250	$280
5			-$250	$240

Which machine would you recommend if the company needs either machine for only 3 years? Assume a MARR of 12%.

(a) Project E1
(b) Project E2
(c) Indifferent
(d) Cannot compare without knowing the year-end salvage values over their service lives.

Solution:

Given: two project cash flows with unequal service lives, MARR = 12%, required service period = 3 years

Find: least cost project

Approach: With the required service period of 3 years, no adjustment to the cash flows for Project E1 is required. However, if Project E2 is selected, it will be used only for 3 years, and we must recognize the unused value of the project (salvage value). Any cash flows occurring after 3 years can be ignored. Since both projects have the same service life after this adjustment, we can use the present value criterion.

$$PW(12\%)_{E1} = -\$400 - \$300(P/A,12\%,3) + \$150(P/F,12\%,3)$$
$$= -\$1,013.78$$
$$PW(12\%)_{E2} = -\$600 - \$250(P/A,12\%,3) + \$320(P/F,12\%,3)$$
$$= -\$972.68$$

Project B is the least cost alternative.

Chapter 6 Annual Equivalence Analysis

6s.1 The annual equivalent of an income stream of $1,000 per year, to be received at the end of each of the next 3 years, at an interest rate of 12% is

(a) $1,000 per year

(b) less than $1,000 per year

(c) greater than $1,000 per year

(d) $1,000(*A/P*, 12%, 3)

Solution:

> Given: $A = \$1,000$, $N = 3$, and MARR $= 12\%$
> Find: AE(12%)
> Approach: The annual equivalent of a constant stream of cash flow series is $1,000, regardless of interest rate used. The answer is (c).

6s.2 Find the annual equivalent worth for the following infinite cash flow series at an interest rate of 10%:

n	Net Cash Flow
0	0
1 -- 10	$400
11 -- ∞	$500

(a) $461.20 (b) $438.60

(c) $445.20 (d) $985.40

Solution:

> Given: cash flow series above
> Find: AE(10%)
> Approach: Since the $400 series extends over the infinite period, we only need to find the equivalent annual worth for the remaining $100 series which is delayed by 10 years.

$$AE(10\%) = \$400 + \frac{\left[\dfrac{\$100}{0.10}(P/F,10\%,10)\right]}{0.10}$$

$$= \$400 + \$100(0.3855)$$

$$= \$438.55$$

6s.3 A local county is considering purchasing some dump trucks for the trash pickups. Each truck will cost $55,000 and have an operating and maintenance cost that starts at $18,000 the first year and increases by $3,000 per year. Assume the salvage value is $12,000 at the end of 5 years and the interest rate is 10%. The equivalent annual cost of owning and operating each truck is most nearly

(a) $35,974   (b) $32,600

(c) $6,956   (d) $37,939

Solution:

Given: $I = \$55{,}000$, $S = \$12{,}000$, $N = 5$ years, O&M costs (a gradient series with $A_1 = \$18{,}000$ and $G = \$3{,}000$), $i = 10\%$

Find: AE(10%)

Approach:

$$AE(10\%)_{\text{ownership cost}} = (\$55{,}000 - \$12{,}000)(A/P,10\%,5) + (0.10)(\$12{,}000)$$

$$= \$12{,}543.29$$

$$AE(10\%)_{\text{O\&M costs}} = \$18{,}000 + \$3{,}000(A/G,10\%,5)$$

$$= \$23{,}430.30$$

$$AE(10\%)_{\text{Total}} = \$35{,}973.59$$

6s.4 Your firm has purchased an injection molding machine at a cost of $100,000. The machine's useful life is estimated at 8 years. Your accounting department has estimated the capital cost for this machine at about $25,455 per year. If your firm's MARR is 20%, how much salvage value do you think the accounting department assumed at the end of 8 years?

(a) $11,000   (b) $12,000

(c) $10,000   (d) $9,000

$25{,}455 = 100{,}000 - S(A/P,20\%) + (0.20)(S)$

Solution:

Given: $I = \$100{,}000$, $N = 8$ years, capital cost = $25,455 per year, and MARR = 20%

Find: S

$$\$25,455 = (\$100,000 - S)(A/P, 20\%, 8) + (0.20)S$$
$$= \$26,061 - 0.2606S + 0.2S$$
$$0.606S = \$606$$
$$S = \$10,000$$

6s.5 You purchased a CNC machine for $18,000. It is expected to have a useful life of 10 years and a salvage value of $3,000. At $i = 15\%$, what is the annual capital cost of this machine?

(a) $3,900   (b) $2,990

(c) $3,740   (d) $3,440

Solution:

Given: $I = \$18,000$, $N = 10$ years, $S = \$3,000$, and MARR $= 15\%$
Find: Capital (ownership) cost

$$CR(10\%) = (\$18,000 - \$3,000)(A/P, 15\%, 10) + (0.20)\$3,000$$
$$= \$3,438.78$$

6s.6 What is the annual equivalent amount at $i = 10\%$ for a series of annual receipts of $500 for the first 10 years, which will increase to $1,000 per year after 10 years, and which will remain constant for the next 10 years?

(a) $634   (b) $650

(c) $713   (d) $750

Solution:

Given: Cash flow series defined above, and MARR $= 10\%$
Find: AE(10%)

$$AE(10\%) = \$500 + \$500(F/A, 10\%, 10)(A/F, 10\%, 20)$$
$$= \$500 + \$134.42$$
$$= \$634.42$$

6s.7 You just purchased a pin inserting machine to relieve some bottleneck problems that have been created in manufacturing a PC board. The machine cost $56,000 and has an estimated service life of 5 years. At that time, the estimated salvage value would be $5,000. The machine is expected to operate 2,500 hours per year. The expected annual operating and maintenance cost would be $6,000. If your firm's interest rate is 15%, what would be the machine cost per hour *without* considering income tax?

(a) $8.79   (b) $5.89

(c) $11.85   (d) $7.85

Solution:

Given: $I = \$56,000$, $S = \$5,000$, $N = 5$ years, annual operating hours = 2,500 hours, O&M = $6,000 per year, and MARR = 15%

Find: Cost per hour

- Capital cost:

$$CR(15\%) = (\$56,000 - \$5,000)(A/P,15\%,5) + \$5,000(0.15)$$

$$= \$15,964$$

- O&M cost: $6,000 per year

- Total annual equivalent cost:

$$AE(15\%) = \$15,964 + \$6,000 = \$21,964$$

- Cost per operating hour:

$$\frac{\$21,964}{2,500} = \$8.79/\text{hour}$$

6s.8 The City of Greenville has decided to build a softball complex on land donated by one of the city residents. The city council has already voted to fund the project at a level of $800,000 (initial capital investment). The city engineer has collected the following financial information for the project.

- Annual upkeep costs: $120,000
- Annual utility costs: $13,000
- Renovation costs: $50,000 for every 5 years
- Annual team user fees (revenues): $32,000
- Useful life: Infinite
- Interest rate: 5%.

If the city expects 40,000 visitors to the complex each year, what should be the minimum ticket price per person, so that the city can break-even?

(a) $2.50 < price ≤ $3.00

(b) $3.00 < price ≤ $3.50

(c) $3.50 < \text{price} \le \$4.00$

(d) $4.00 < \text{price} \le \$4.50$

Solution:

Given: $I = \$800,000$, $N = $ infinite, other financial data given above, number of visitors per year $= 40,000$, MARR $= 5\%$

Find: break-even ticket price

$$CR(5\%) = \$800,000(A/P,15\%,\infty)$$

$$= \$800,000(0.05)$$

$$= \$40,000$$

$$O\&M = \$120,000 + \$13,000 - \$32,000$$

$$= \$101,000$$

$$\text{Renovation cost} = \$50,000(A/F,5\%,5)$$

$$= \$9,049$$

$$AE(5\%) = \$40,000 + \$101,000 + \$9,049$$

$$= \$150,048$$

$$\text{Cost per ticket} = \frac{\$150,048}{40,000} = \$3.75 \text{ per ticket}$$

Comments: Note that the 5-year cycle recurring renovation cost can be converted into an equivalent annual cost by using the A/F factor.

6s.9 Consider manufacturing equipment that has an installed cost of $100K. The equipment is expected to generate $30K of annual energy savings during its first year of installation. The value of these annual savings is expected to increase by 3% per year because of increased fuel costs. Assume that the equipment has a service life of 5 years (or 3,000 operating hours per year) with no appreciable salvage value. Determine the equivalent dollar savings per each operating hour at $i = 14\%$.

(a) $1.300 per hour

(b) $1.765 per hour

(c) $0.827 per hour

(d) $0.568 per hour.

Solution:

Given: $I = \$100K$, $S = 0$, annual savings $= \$30K$ (first year) and grow by 3% per year, $N = 5$ years, annual operating hours $= 3,000$, $i = 14\%$

Find: Savings per hour

$$PW(14\%) = -\$100,000 + \$30(P/A_1,3\%,14\%,5)$$

$$= -\$100,000 + \$30,000\left[\frac{1-(1+0.03)^5(1+0.14)^{-5}}{0.14-0.03}\right]$$

$$= -\$100,000 + \$30,000[3.6174]$$

$$= \$8,520.73$$

$$AE(14\%) = \$8,520.73(A/P,14\%,5)$$

$$= \$2,481.95$$

$$\text{Savings per hour} = \frac{\$2,481.95}{3,000}$$

$$= \$0.83/\text{hour}$$

6s.10 Colgate Printing Co. (CPC) has the book binding contract for the Ralph Brown library. The library pays $25 per book to CPC. CPC binds 1,000 books every year for the library. Ralph Brown library is considering the option of binding the books in-house in the basement of the library complex. In order to do this, the library would have to invest in a binding machine and other printing equipment at a cost of $100,000. The useful life of the machine is 12 years, at the end of which time, the machine is estimated to have a salvage value of $12,000. The annual operating and maintenance costs of the machine are estimated to be $10,000. Assuming an interest rate of 6%, what is the cost of binding per book for the in-house option?

(a) $11.22 per book
(b) $17.33 per book
(c) $21.22 per book
(d) $25.15 per book

Solution:

Given: $I = \$100,000$, $S = \$12,000$, O&M costs = $10,000 per year, annual binding volume = 1,000 units, $N = 12$ years, and MARR = 6%
Find: book binding cost per unit

- Capital cost:

$$CR(6\%) = (\$100,000 - \$12,000)(A/P,6\%,12) + (0.06)(\$12,000)$$
$$= \$11,216$$

- Operating cost: $10,000
- Total equivalent annual cost: $21,216
- Cost per book:

$$\frac{\$21,216}{1,000} = \$21.22 \text{ per book}$$

6s.11 In Problem 6s.10, what annual volume of books in need of binding would make both the options (in-house versus subcontracting) equivalent?

(a) $850 copies   (b) $900 copies

(c) $1,166 copies   (d) $1,096 copies

Solution:

Given: Financial data given in 6s.11
Find: Break-even volume
Approach:

$$\frac{\$21,216}{X} = \$25$$
$$X = 848.64$$

6s.12 The following infinite cash flow series has a rate of return of 10%. Determine the unknown value of X.

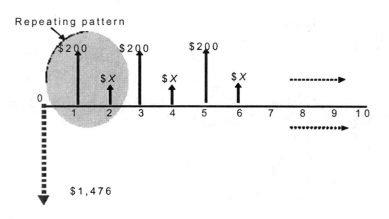

68

(a) $82   (c) $90

(b) $100   (d) $120

Solution:

<u>Given</u>: an infinite steam of cash flow series with a repeating pattern

<u>Find</u>: X such that the capitalized equivalent worth will be $1,476

<u>Approach</u>:

$$\frac{[\$200(F/P,10\%,1)+X](A/F,10\%,2)}{0.10}=\$1,476$$

$$\frac{\$220(0.4762)+0.4762X}{0.10}=\$1,476$$

$$\$104.76+0.4762X=\$147.60$$

$$X=\$89.90$$

6s.13 The owner of a workshop is planning to purchase a special machine for $50,000. The annual operating cost (such as fuel, labor, and power) is expected to be $8,000 per year. If the machine has a useful life of 12 years, what is the minimum required annual equivalent revenue needed to break even with an 8% annual interest rate? Assume that the machine would have an estimated market value of $5,000 at the end of its useful life.

(a) $5,972   (c) $8,000

(b) $6,372   (d) $14,371

Solution:

<u>Given</u>: $I = \$50,000$, $S = \$5,000$, O&M = $8,000 per year, $N = 12$ years, and MARR = 8%

<u>Find</u>: required annual revenue to break-even

<u>Approach</u>:

$$AE(8\%) = (\$500,000 - \$5,000)(A/P,8\%,12) + \$5,000(0.08)$$

$$+\$8,000$$

$$= \$14,371$$

69

6s.14 Suppose that a young investor is considering investing $100 in an interest bearing account that pays 10% interest compounded annually. The investor's plan is to leave the money in the account for one year and then withdraw the principal plus all accrued interest. If the investor's MARR is known to be 10%, does the investor:

(a) Increase his/her wealth by an additional $10

(b) Break even on the investment

(c) The investor earns an additional $10 and also breaks even on the investment

(d) None of the above

Solution:

> Given: Principal = $100, investment interest = 10% per year, $N = 1$, and MARR = 10%
> Find: which statement is correct?
>
>
> The correct answer is (b).
>
> Comments: The meaning of MARR of 10% is the required return on your investment. Since your investment brings in *exactly* a 10% return on your investment, there will be no change in your net worth before or after your investment. For example, if you do not invest your $100 in this interest bearing account, you will continue to earn a 10% return from other investment opportunities. That is the definition of MARR, the opportunity cost foregone.

6s.15 What is the annual equivalent amount at $i = 10\%$ for the payment series with the first payment in the amount of $2,000 occurring at $n = 2$ and the second payment in the amount of $4,000 at n = 4, the third payment in the amount of $6,000 at $n = 6$.

(a) $2,000   (c) $1,923

(b) $1,874   (d) $1,784

Solution:

> Given: cash flow series = $(A_2 = \$2,000; A_4 = \$4,000; A_6 = \$6,000)$, and MARR = 10%
> Find: AE(10%)
> Approach:

70

$$AE(10\%) = \$2,000(P/F,10\%,2) + \$4,000(P/F,10\%,4)$$
$$+\$6,000(P/F,10\%,6)$$
$$= (\$7,771.78)(A/P,10\%,6)$$
$$= \$1,784.45$$

6s.16 A consumer product company is considering introducing a new shaving system called DELTA-4 in the market. The company plans to manufacture 75 million units of DELTA-4 a year. The investment at time 0 that is required for building the manufacturing plant is estimated as $500 million, and the economic life of the project is assumed to be 10 years. The annual total operating expenses, including manufacturing costs and overheads, are estimated as $175 million. The salvage value that can be realized from the project is estimated as $120 million. If the company's MARR is 25%, determine the minimum price that the company should charge for a DELTA-4 shaving system. (Do not consider any income tax effect.)

(a) $3.15   (c) $5.15

(b) $4.15   (d) $2.80

Solution:

Given: $I = \$500M$, $S = \$120M$, $N = 10$ years, O&M = $175M, annual production volume = 75 million units, and MARR = 25%
Find: break-even sales price per unit (before tax)
Approach:
$$AE(25\%) = (\$500M - \$120M)(A/P,25\%,10) + \$120M(0.25)$$
$$+\$175M$$
$$= \$311.4276M$$
$$\text{Cost per unit} = \frac{\$311.4276M}{75M} = \$4.15/\text{unit}$$

6s.17 Two options are available for painting your house: (1) Oil-based painting, which costs $5,000 and (2) water-based painting, which costs $3,000. The estimated lives are 10 years and 5 years respectively. For either option, no salvage value will remain at the end of respective service lives. Assume that you will keep and maintain the house for 10 years. If your personal interest rate is 10% per year, which of the following statement is correct?

(a) On an annual basis, Option 1 will cost about $850

(b) On an annual basis, Option 2 is about $22 cheaper than Option 1

(c) On an annual basis, both options cost about the same

(d) On an annual basis, Option 2 will cost about $820.

Solution:

Given: $I = (\$5,000, \$3,000)$, $S = (0, 0)$, $N = (10, 5)$, and MARR = 10%

Find: which option is cheaper and by how much?

Approach:

- Oil-based painting (one-cycle):

$$AE(10\%) = \$5,000(A/P,10\%,10) = \$813.73$$

- Water-based painting (two-cycle):

$$AE(10\%) = \$3,000(A/P,10\%,5) = \$791.39$$

Comments: Here we assume that, if you go with the water-based painting, you will need to repaint the house at the end of year 5. However, you only need to calculate the AE based on the first cycle. The annual difference is $22 in favor of the water-based painting option.

6s.18 Two 150-horsepower (HP) motors are being considered for installation at a municipal sewage-treatment plant. The first motor costs $4,500 and has an operating efficiency of 83% at full load. The second motor costs $3,600 and has an efficiency rating of 80% at full load. Both motors are projected to have zero salvage value after a life of 10 years. The annual operating and maintenance cost (excepting power cost) amounts to 15% of the original cost of each motor. The power costs are a flat 5 cents per kilowatt-hour. The minimum number of hours of full-load operation per year necessary to justify the purchase of the more expensive motor at $i = 6\%$ falls in which one of the following ranges?

(a) 800 hours to 850 hours

(b) 851 hours to 900 hours

(c) 901 hours to 950 hours

(d) 951 hours to 1,000 hours

(e) 1,001 hours to 1,050 hours.

Solution:

Given: motor capacity = 150HP, efficiency factor (0.83, 0.80), $I = (\$4,500, \$3,600)$, $N = (10, 10)$, $S = (0, 0)$, energy cost = $0.05 kw/hr, maintenance cost = ($675, $540), MARR = 6%

Find: Break-even operating hours

Approach: Required input power: $150\text{HP} \times 0.746 \text{ KW/HP} = 111.9 \text{ KW}$

- Motor A:
  - Capital cost:
  $$CR(6\%) = \$4,500(A/P,6\%,10) = \$611.41$$
  - Operating cost:

  $$(0.05)\frac{111.9(X)}{0.83} + 0.15(\$4,500) = 6.741X + 675$$

  - Total cost:

  $$AE(6\%)_{\text{Motor A}} = \$1,86.41 + 6.741X$$

- Motor B:
  - Capital cost:
  $$CR(6\%) = \$3,600(A/P,6\%,10) = \$489.12$$
  - Operating cost:

  $$(0.05)\frac{111.9(X)}{0.80} + 0.15(\$3,600) = 6.9938X + 540$$

  - Total cost:
  $$AE(6\%)_{\text{Motor B}} = \$1,029.12 + 6.9938X$$

- Break-even operating hours:

$$AE(6\%)_{\text{Motor A}} = AE(6\%)_{\text{Motor B}}$$
$$\$1,86.41 + 6.741X = \$1,029.12 + 6.9938X$$
$$0.2528X = 257.29$$
$$X_{\text{break-even}} = 1,018 \text{ hours}$$

Chapter 7 Rate of Return Analysis

7s.1 You are considering an investment that costs $2,000. It is expected to have a useful life of 3 years. You are very confident about the revenues during the first and the third year, but you are unsure about the revenue in year 2. If you hope to make at least a 10% rate of return on your investment ($2,000), what should be the minimum revenue in year 2?

Year	Cash Flow
0	-$2,000
1	1,000
2	X
3	1,200

(a) $290 (b) $260
(c) $230 (d) $190.

Solution:

Given: cash flow series, rate of return = 10%, $N = 3$ years
Find: X
Approach: If the rate of return is known to be 10%, the net present value of the cash flow series at this rate of return should be zero.

$$0 = -\$2,000 + \$1,000(P/F,10\%,1) + X(P/F,10\%,2)$$
$$+\$1,200(P/F,10\%,3)$$
$$0.8264X = \$189.33$$
$$X = \$229.08$$

7s.2 If you purchase stock for $100 now, what is the rate of return on your investment if the stock is worth $337.50 at the end of 3 years?

(a) 75.80%   (c) 33.75%
(b) 25%   (d) 50%

Solution:

Given: $P = \$100$, $F = \$33.50$, $N = 3$ years
Find: i^*

Approach: Use the $(F/P, i, N)$ factor to establish equivalence between P and F.

$$\$100(F/P, i, 3) = \$337.50$$
$$\$100(1+i)^3 = \$337.50$$
$$i = 50\%$$

7s.3 You are considering an open-pit mining operation. The cash flow pattern is somewhat unusual since you must invest in some mining equipment, operate them for 2 years, and restore the sites to their original condition. You estimate the net cash flows to be as follows:

n	Cash Flows
0	-$1,600,000
1	1,500,000
2	1,500,000
3	-700,000

What is the approximate rate of return of this investment?

(a) 25% (b) 38%
(c) 42% (d) 62%

Solution:

Given: cash flow series, $N = 3$ years
Find: i^*
Approach: Note that the project is a nonsimple investment as there are more than one sign changes in the net cash flow series. This indicates the possibility of having multiple rates of return. In fact, there are two rates of return—(38.61%, -61.93%).

The correct answer is (b).

7s.4 You are considering a CNC machine that costs $150,000. This machine will have an estimated service life of 10 years with a net after-tax salvage value of $15,000. Its annual after-tax operating and maintenance costs are estimated to be $50,000. To expect an 18% rate of return on investment after-tax, what would be the required minimum annual after-tax revenues?

(a) $63,500   (b) $82,740
(c) $92,435   (d) $94,568.

Solution:

Given: $I = \$150,000$, $S = \$15,000$, annual O&M costs = $\$50,000$, rate of return = 18%, $N = 10$ years

Find: required annul after-tax revenue to achieve an 18% rate of return

Approach: If the rate of return is known to be 18%, the annual equivalent value of the cash flow series at this rate of return should be also zero.

Capital cost:

$$CR(18\%) = (\$150,000 - \$15,000)(A/P, 18\%, 10) + \$15,000(0.18) = \$32,739$$

Annul O&M cost: $50,000

Annual Equivalent Cost:

$$AEC = \$32,739 + \$50,000 = \$82,739$$

Required annual A/T revenue to breakeven = $82,739

7s.5 Find the rate of return for the following infinite cash flow series.

Year	Cash Flow
0	-$15,459
1	3,000
2	3,000
⋮	⋮

(a) 15%   (b) 515.30%

(c) 19.41%   (d) 17.83%.

Solution:

Given: cash flow series, $N = 8$ years

Find: rate of return

Approach: Since we are dealing with an infinite cash flow stream, use the capitalized equivalent worth formula, which is A/i.

$$CE(i) = \frac{A}{i}$$

$$\$15,459 = \frac{\$3,000}{i}$$

$$i = 19.41\%$$

7s.6 Consider the investment project with the following Net Cash Flows.

Year	Net Cash Flow
0	-$1,500
1	$X
2	$650
3	$X

What would be the value of X if the project's IRR is 10%?

(a) $425   (c) $580

(b) $1,045   (d) $635

Solution:

Given: cash flow series, IRR = 10%, $N = 3$ years
Find: X
Approach: If the rate of return is known to be 10%, the net present value of the cash flow series at this rate of return should be zero.

$$PW(10\%) = -\$1,500 + \frac{X}{1.1} + \frac{\$650}{1.1^2} + \frac{X}{1.1^3} = 0$$

$$\$1,500 = 0.9091X + \$537.19 + 0.7513X$$

$$\$962.81 = 1.6604X$$

$$X = \$579.87$$

7s.7 A manufacturing company is considering two types of industrial projects that require the same level of initial investment but provide different levels of operating cash flows over the project life. The in-house engineer has compiled the following financial data related to both projects, including the rate of return figures.

The company has been using the internal rate of return as a project justification tool, and these projects will be evaluated based on the principle of rate of return. The firm's minimum required rate of return is known to be 12%. Which project should you select?

	Net Cash Flow		Incremental
n	Project A	Project B	(A - B)
0	-$18,000	-$18,000	0
1	960	11,600	-10,640
2	7,400	6,500	900
3	13,100	4,000	9,100
4	7,560	3,122	4,438
$i*$	18%	20%	14.72%

(a) Select A, because its increment of investment exceeds 12%.

(b) Select B, because its rate of return is higher than A with the same initial investment.

(c) Select B, because it recovers most of investment during the first year.

(d) Select B, because it can generate 20% profit (as opposed to 18% for project A) for every dollar invested.

Solution:

Given: two cash flow series with known IRRs, $N = 4$ years

Find: which project to select

Approach: Use an incremental analysis to select the correct project. In doing so, create an incremental investment cash flow series by subtracting the lower cost investment from the higher cost one. If the initial investment is the same for both alternatives, go to the next period to see if there is an incremental investment cash flow series that can be created.

The correct answer is (a), since $IRR_{A-B} > 12\%$.

7s.8 Consider the following investment projects.

Year (n)	Net Cash Flow	
	Project 1	Project 2
0	-$1,200	-$2,000
1	600	1,500
2	1,000	1,000
IRR	19.65%	17.54%

Determine the range of MARR where project 2 would be preferred over project 1.

(a) MARR = 12.5%
(b) 13% = MARR = 15%
(c) 16% = MARR
(d) Not enough information to determine.

Solution:

Given: two cash flow series, $N = 2$ years
Find: the range of MARR where Project 2 is preferred
Approach: First create an incremental investment cash flow series by subtracting Project 1 from Project 2. Then determine the rate of return on this incremental investment.

n	Cash Flows (2 – 1)
0	-$800
1	900
2	0

IRR $_{2-1}$ = 12.5%, indicating that Project 2 would be preferred over Project 1 when MARR < 12.5%. The correct answer is (a).

7s.9 Consider the following two investment situations:

- In 1970, when Wal-Mart Stores, Inc. went public, an investment of 100 shares cost $1,650. That investment would have been worth $2,991,080 after 25 years. The Wal-Mart investors' rate of return would be around 35%.

- In 1980, if you bought 100 shares of Fidelity Mutual Funds, it would have cost $5,245. That investment would have been worth $80,810 after 15 years.

Which of the following statement is correct?

(a) If you bought only 50 shares of the Wal-Mart stocks in 1970 and kept it for 25 years, your rate of return would be 0.5 times 35%.

(b) The investors in Fidelity Mutual Funds would have made profit at the annual rate of 30% on the funds remaining invested.

(c) If you bought 100 shares of Wal-Mart in 1970 but sold them after 10 years. (Assume that the Wal-Mart stocks grew at the annual rate of 35% for the first 10 years.) Then immediately, you put all the proceeds into Fidelity Mutual Funds. After 15 years, the total worth of your investment would be around $511,140.

(d) None of the above.

Solution:

Given: financial data as provided

Find: the correct statement

Approach: To see if each statement is correct, you need to calculate the required

(a) Incorrect-- The rate of return is not scaled by the amount of investment. The rate of return on investment is still 35% whether you own 1 share or 100 shares.

(b) Incorrect--$5,245(1 + i)^{15} = \$80,810$ or $i = 20\%$, which is much less than 30%.

(c) Correct

Investment worth at the end of 10 years:

$1,650(F / P,35\%,10) = \$33,175.82$

Investment worth at the end of 25 years:

$33,175.82(F / P,20\%,15) = \$511,140.57$

(d) Incorrect

7s.10 The following information on two revenue projects is given:

- IRR of project A = 16%.

- IRR of project B = 16%.

- Both projects have a service life of 6 years and need the same initial investment of $23,000.

- IRR on incremental cash flows (A–B) = 14%.

If your MARR is 20%, which of the following statements is correct?

(a) Select A.

(b) Select B.

(c) Select either one of the projects.

(d) Select neither project.

(e) Information is insufficient to make a decision.

Solution:

Given: financial facts

Find: the correct statement

Approach: Each project must be justified on its own merit. That is , the rate of return must exceed 20%. Since both projects fail to meet this requirement, the correct answer is (d).

7s.11 The following data contains a summary of how a project's balance changes over its 3-year service life for two different interest rates of $i = 10\%$ and $i = 15\%$.

	Project Balance	
End of Period	$i = 10\%$	$i = 15\%$
0	-$1,000	-$1,000
1	-$850	-$900
2	-$400	-$500
3	0	-$1,350

Which of the following statements is correct?

(a) The IRR of the project should be 15%.

(b) The IRR of the project should be greater than 10%.

(c) The IRR of the project should be equal to 10%.

(d) It is not possible to determine the IRR from the given data.

Solution:

Given: project balances at 10% and 15% respectively, rate of return = 10%, $N = 3$ years

Find: X

Approach: If the rate of return is known to be 10%, the terminal project balance at this rate of return should be zero.

The correct answer is (c).

7s.12 Consider the following cash flow series. Assume that the firm's MARR is 10%.

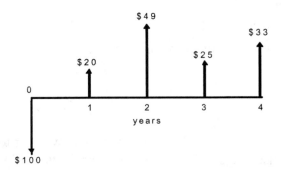

Which of the following statements is *incorrect?*

    (a)   The project's net future worth is zero.

    (b)   The project's net present worth is zero.

    (c)   The project's IRR is zero.

    (d)   The project's annual equivalent is zero.

Solution:

Given: cash flow series, MARR $= 10\%$, $N = 4$ years

Find: the incorrect statement

Approach: If the rate of return is known to be 10%, the net present value of the cash flow series at this rate of return should be zero.

$$FW(10\%) = -\$100(F/P,10\%,4) + \$20(F/P,10\%,3) + \$49(F/P,10\%,2)$$
$$+\$25(F/P,10\%,1) + \$33$$
$$\cong 0$$
$$PW(10\%) = AE(10\%) = 0$$

The incorrect statement is (c). The project's IRR is 10%.

7s.13 The following information on two mutually exclusive projects is given below:

n	Project A	Project B
0	-3,000	-5,000
1	1,350	1,350
2	1,800	1,800

| 3 | 1,500 | 5,406 |
| IRR | 25% | 25% |

Which of the following statements is *correct?*

(a) Since the two projects have the same rate of return, they are indifferent.

(b) Project A would be a better choice, as the required investment is smaller with the same rate of return.

(c) Project B would be a better choice as long as the investor's MARR is less than 25%.

(d) Project B is a better choice regardless of the investor's MARR.

Solution:

Given: two cash flow series with known IRRs, $N = 3$ years
Find: the correct statement
Approach: When we compare mutually exclusive investment projects based on the rate of return principle, we must apply the incremental analysis.

n	Project A	Project B	Project B – Project A
0	-$3,000	-$5,000	-$2,000
1	1,350	1,350	0
2	1,800	1,800	0
3	1,500	5,406	$3,906
IRR	25%	25%	25%

The correct answer is (c), as Project B would be preferred over Project A as long as the MARR is less than 15%.

7s.14 The following infinite cash flow has a rate of return of 15%. Compute the unknown value of X.

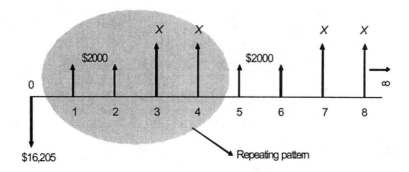

83

(a) $2,542   (c) $3,640
(b) $3,000   (d) $5,644

Solution:

Given: cash flow series, rate of return = 15%, $N = \infty$ years

Find: X

Approach: If the rate of return of the project is known to be 15%, the present value of the infinite cash flow stream should be $16,205. In finding the unknown value of X, we need to find the annual equivalent value of the cash flows of the first cycle. Once we determine the equivalent annual value, we use the capitalized equivalent worth formula, $CE(i) = A/i$.

$$AE(15\%)_{\text{first cycle}} = \$2,000 + [(X - 2,000) + 1.15(X - 2,000)](A/F, 15\%, 4)$$
$$= \$2,000 + 0,4306X - \$861.14$$

$$CE(15\%)_{\text{infinite stream}} = \frac{\$1,138.86 + 0.4306X}{0.15} = \$16,205$$

$$X = \$3,000$$

7s.15 You are considering purchasing a $1,000 bond with a coupon rate of 9.5%, interest payable annually. If the current inflation rate is 4% per year, which will continue in the foreseeable future, what would be the real rate of return if you sold the bond at $1,080 after 2 years?

(a) about 8.9%   (b) about 9.5%
(c) about 13.26%   (d) about 9.26%

Solution:

Given: $I = \$1,000$, coupon rate = 9.5% per year, $f = 4\%$, rate of return = 10%, $N = 2$ years

Find: real rate of return

Approach: First find the yield to maturity (or rate of return) of the bond. Then, find the real rate of return.

Yield to maturity:

$$\$1,000 = \$95(P/A, i, 2) + \$1,080(P/F, i, 2)$$

$$i = 13.25\%$$

Real rate of return:

$$i' = \frac{i - f}{1 + f} = \frac{0.1325 - 0.04}{1 + 0.04} = 8.89\%$$

7s.16 A regional airport is considering installing a new baggage handling system. Two different vendors submitted their bids on the system. The airport is to replace its current system. The cash flows that describe each baggage handling system with respect to the current system are given below.

Year (n)	Vendor A	Vendor B	Vendor B – Vendor A
0	-$500,000	-$600,000	-$100,000
1 - 15	48,170	65,880	17,710
IRR	5%	7%	15.73%

Using the rate of return as the decision criterion, which of the following statement is correct?

(a) Vendor B is preferred as long as the airport's MARR is less than equal to 15.73%
(b) Vendor A is preferred as long as the airport's MARR is less than 5%.
(c) Vendor B is preferred as long as the airport's MARR is less than 7%.
(d) Vendor A is preferred if the airport's MARR is greater than 15.73%.
(e) None of the above.

Solution:

    <u>Given</u>: two mutually exclusive projects and its incremental cash flows
    <u>Find</u>: the correct statement
    <u>Approach</u>: Note that if the airport's MARR exceeds 5%, Vendor A is no longer viable option. If MARR > 7%, both vendors are eliminated.

    The correct statement is (c).

Chapter 8 Accounting for Depreciation and Income Taxes

8s.1 A machine, purchased for $45,000, has a depreciable life of 4 years. It will have an expected salvage value of $5,000 at the end of the depreciable life. Using the straight-line method, what is the book value at the end of year 2?

(a) $27,500   (b) $20,000

(c) $35,000   (d) $25,000.

Solution:

Given: $I = \$45,000$, $S = \$5,000$, $N = 4$ years, and SL depreciation

Find: B_2

$$D_1 = D_2 = \frac{(\$45,000 - \$5,000)}{4} = \$10,000$$

$$B_2 = B_0 - D_1 - D_2 = \$45,000 - 2(\$10,000)$$

$$= \$45,000 - \$20,000 = \$25,000$$

8s.2 Consider problem 8s.1. If the double declining balance (200% DB) method is used, what is the depreciation amount for year 2?

(a) $10,000   (b) $11,250

(c) $20,000   (d) $17,500.

Solution:

Given: $I = \$45,000$, $S = \$5,000$, $N = 4$ years, and DB depreciation

Find: D_2

Step 1: Find the declining balance rate (α) to be used.

$$\alpha = 2(\frac{1}{4}) = 50\%$$

Step 2: Find the depreciation amount each year as follows.

$$D_1 = 0.5(\$45,000) = \$22,500$$

$$D_2 = 0.5(\$45,000 - D_1) = \$11,250$$

8s.3 Consider problem 8s.2. Suppose the estimated salvage value at the end of year 4 is estimated to be $10,000, instead of $5,000. If the 200% method is used, what is the depreciation amount for year 3?

(a) $5,625   (b) $10,000

(c) $12,000   (d) $18,000.

Solution:

Given: $I = \$45,000$, $S = \$10,000$, $N = 4$ years, and 200% DB depreciation

Find: B_3

$$\alpha = 2(\frac{1}{4}) = 50\%$$

$$D_1 = 0.5(\$45,000) = \$22,500$$

$$D_2 = 0.5(\$45,000 - D_1) = \$11,250$$

$$D_3 = 0.5(\$45,000 - D_1 - D_2) = \$5,625$$

$$B_3 = B_2 - D_3 = \$11,250 - \$5,625 = \$5,625 < S$$

Recalculated D_3 and B_3 :

$$D_3 = \$1,250$$

$$B_3 = \$10,000$$

8s.4 Your accounting records indicate that an asset in use has a book value of $8,640. The asset cost $30,000 when it was purchased, and it has been depreciated under the 5 MACRS method. Based on the information available, determine how many years the asset has been in service.

(a) 3 years   (b) 4 years

(c) 5 years   (d) 6 years.

Solution:

Given: $I = \$30,000$, $B_n = \$8,640$, and 5-year MACRS depreciation

Find: n (the number of years in service)

n	MACRS	D_n	B_n
0			$30,000
1	20%	$6,000	$24,000
2	32%	$9,600	$14,400
3	19.20%	$5,760	$8,640
4	11.52%	$3,456	
5	11.52%	$3,456	
6	5.76%	$1,728	

The correct answer is 3 years.

8s.5 Which of the following statements is correct?

   (a) The reason why the U.S. Congress allows business to use MACRS depreciation as opposed to conventional methods is to reduce the business tax burden over the project life.

   (b) Under the declining balance depreciation system, it is always desirable to switch to straight-line depreciation.

   (c) When determining the cost basis for an asset's depreciation, you must include all the costs that were incurred to keep the asset in operable condition.

   (d) The main reason why a typical firm may use a straight-line depreciation method in reporting an income to outside investors (as opposed to any other accelerated tax depreciation methods) is to abide by the accounting principle—that is to report the true cost of doing business.

Solution:

   Given: Statements above
   Find: the correct statement

   The answer is (c).

8s.6 A company purchased a drill press priced at $170,000 in year 0. The company additionally incurred $30,000 for site preparation and labor to install the machine. The drill press is classified as a 7-year MACRS class property. The company is considering selling the drill press for $70,000 at the end of year 4. Compute the book value at the end of year 4 that should be used in calculating the taxable gains.

   (a) $62,480

   (b) $53,108

   (c) $63,725

   (d) $74,970.

Solution:

   Given: $I = \$170,000$, site preparation $= \$30,000$, market price $= \$70,000$ at end of year 4, and 7-year MACRS depreciation
   Find: B_4

$$\text{Depreciation base} = \$170,000 + \$30,000 = \$200,000$$
$$B_4 = \$200,000 - (D_1 + D_2 + D_3 + D_4)$$
$$= \$200,000 - \$200,000(0.1429 + 0.2449 + 0.1749 + 0.1249)$$
$$= \$62,480$$

8s.7 Which of the following statements is correct?

(a) Over a project's life, a typical business will generate a greater amount of total project cash flows (undiscounted) if a faster depreciation method is adopted.

(b) No matter which depreciation method you adopt, total tax obligations over a project's life remain unchanged.

(c) Depreciation recapture equals cost basis minus an asset's book value at the time of disposal, that is, if the salvage value is less than the asset's cost basis.

(d) Cash flows normally include depreciation expenses since they represent a cost of doing busine ss.

Solution:

Given: statements above
Find: the correct statement

The correct statement is (b).

8s.8 You purchased a computer system which cost $50,000 5 years ago. At that time, the system was estimated to have a service life of 5 years with salvage value of $5,000. These estimates are still good. The property has been depreciated according to a 5-year MACRS property class. Now (at the end of year 5 from purchase) you are considering selling the computer at $10,000. What book value should you use in determining the taxable gains?

(a) $8,640   (b) $10,368
(c) $5,760   (d) $11,520.

Solution:

Given: $I = \$50,000$, $S = \$5,000$, $N = 5$ years, and 5-year MACRS depreciation
Find: B_5

n	MACRS	D_n	B_n
0			$50,000
1	20%	$10,000	$40,000
2	32%	$16,000	$24,000
3	19.20%	$9,600	$14,400
4	11.52%	$5,760	$8,640
5	11.52%	$5,760	$2,880
6	5.76%	$2,880	0

Since the asset will be disposed of at the end of year 5, the half-year convention must be applied in calculating the depreciation amount in year 5. The adjusted depreciation amount in year 5 is $5,760/2 = $2,880. This results in $B_5 = $5,760$.

8s.9 Omar Shipping Company bought a tugboat for $75,000 (year 0) and expected to use it for 5 years, after which it will be sold for $12,000. Suppose the company estimates the following revenues and expenses from the tugboat investment for the first operating year.

Operating revenue	$200,000
Operating expenses	$84,000
Depreciation	$4,000

If the company pays taxes at the rate of 30% on its taxable income, what is the net income during the first year?

(a) $28,700   (b) $81,200

(c) $78,400   (d) $25,900.

Solution:

Given: Accounting information as provided above
Find: net income in year 1

Tugboat Project	Tax Year 1
Operating revenue	$200,000
Operating expenses	84,000
Depreciation	4,000
Taxable income	112,000
Income taxes (30%)	33,600
Net income	$78,400

8s.10 In Problem 8s.9, assume for the moment that (1) all sales are for cash, and (2) all costs, except depreciation, were paid during year 1. How much cash would have been generated from operations?

(a) $82,400   (b) $32,700

(c) $85,200   (d) $3,400.

Solution:

Given: net income = $78,400 and depreciation = $4,000
Find: net cash flow in year 1

$$\text{Net cash flow from operation} = \text{net income} + \text{depreciation}$$
$$= \$78,400 + \$4,000$$
$$= \$82,400$$

8s.11 Gilbert Corporation had a gross income of $500,000 in tax year 1, $150,000 in salaries, $30,000 in wages, $20,000 in interest, and $60,000 in depreciation expenses for an asset purchased 3 years ago. Ajax Corporation has a gross income of $500,000 in tax year 1, and $150,000 in salaries, $90,000 in wages, and $20,000 in interest expenses. Apply the current tax rates and determine which of the following statements is correct.

(a) Both corporations will pay the same amount of income taxes in year 1.

(b) Both corporations will have the same amount of net cash flows in year 1.

(c) Ajax Corporation will have a larger net cash flow than Gilbert in year 1.

(d) Gilbert Corporation will have a larger taxable income than Ajax Corporation in year 1.

Solution:

Given: financial data as provided above
Find: identify the correct statement using the corporate tax schedule of year 2003

Description	Gilbert Corporation	Ajax Corporation
Gross income	$500,000	$500,000
Expenses:		
Salaries	150,000	150,000
Wages	30,000	90,000
Interest	20,000	20,000
Depreciation	60,000	
Taxable income	$240,000	$240,000
Income taxes	$76,850	$76,850

Net income	$163,150	$163,150
Net cash flow	$223,150	$163,150

The correct statement is (b). Both corporations will have the same amount of net income, but Gilbert will have $60,000 more in net cash flow during the first tax year.

8s.12 A company purchased an industrial fork-lift for $75,000 in year 0. The company expects to use it for the next 7 years after which it plans to sell it for $10,000. The estimated gross income and expenses excluding depreciation for the first year are given below. The fork-lift will be depreciated according to a 5-year MACRS.

	Year 1
Gross revenue	$120,000
Expenses	$40,000
(Depreciation not included)	

Determine the average tax rate applicable in the first year of operation, using the current corporate tax rate schedule.

(a) 15%   (c) 18.75%

(b) 17.31%   (d) 25%.

Solution:

Given: $I = \$75,000$, $S = \$10,000$, $N = 7$ years, 5-year MACRS depreciation, gross revenue = $120,000, and expenses = $40,000
Find: the average tax rate using the corporate tax schedule of year 2003

Gross revenue	$120,000
Expenses	40,000
Depreciation	15,000
Taxable income	$65,000

First $50,000 @15%	$7,500
Remaining $15,000 @25%	$3,750
Total taxes	$11,250

The average tax rate = $11,250/$65,000 = 0.1731

8s.13 Minolta Machine Shop purchased a computer-controlled vertical drill press for $100,000. The drill press is classified as a 3-year MACRS property. Minolta is planning to use the press for 5 years. Then Minolta will sell the press at the end of service life at $20,000. The annual revenues are estimated to be $110,000. If the estimated net cash flow at the end of year 5 is $30,000, what are the estimated operating and maintenance expenses in year 5? Minolta's income tax rate is 40%.

(a) $60,000   (c) $80,000

(b) $65,000   (d) $88,333.

Solution:

Given: $I = \$100,000$, $S = \$20,000$, $N = 5$ years, 3-year MACRS depreciation, annual revenue = $110,000, net cash flow at year 5 = $30,000, and income tax rate = 40%

Find: the operating and maintenance expenses in year 5.

The depreciation expense for year 5 will be zero as the asset would be fully depreciated by then. Therefore, the book value at year 5 will be zero as well. The entire $20,000 is treated as an ordinary income.

	Net Income
Revenue	$110,000
Salvage value	20,000
Expenses:	
O&M	X
Depreciation	0
Taxable income	$130,000 - X$
Income taxes	$52,000 - 0.4X$
Net income	$78,000 - 0.6X$
Net cash flow	$30,000$

Note that the net cash flow is obtained by adding the non-cash expenses (depreciation) to net income,

$$\$30,000 = \$78,000 - 0.6X + \text{Depreciation (\$0)}$$
$$X = \$80,000$$

Chapter 9 Project Cash Flow Analysis

9s.1 J&J Electric Company expects to have taxable income of $320,000 from its regular business over the next two years. The company is considering a new residential wiring project for a proposed apartment complex during year 0. This 2-year project requires purchase of new equipment for $30,000. The equipment falls into the MACRS 5-year class. The equipment will be sold after 2 years for $12,000. The project will bring in additional revenue of $100,000 each year, but it sis expected to incur an additional operating cost of $40,000 each year. What is the income tax rate to use in year 1 for this project evaluation?

(a) 39%   (b) 34%   (c) 33.77%   (d) 35.39%

Solution:

Given: accounting and cash flow data
Find: income tax rate to use in project year 1
Approach: find the taxable incomes and income taxes with and without project

Revenue	$100,000
Expenses	40,000
Depreciation	6,000
Taxable income	$ 54,000

	Before Project	After Project	Due to Project
Taxable income	$320,000	$374,000	$54,000
Income taxes	108,050	127,160	19,110
Tax rate	33.77%	34%	35.39%

9s.2 Consider the following financial data for an investment project:

- Required capital investment at $n = 0$: $100,000
- Project service life: 10 years
- Salvage value at $n = 10$: $15,000
- Annual revenue: $150,000
- Annual O&M costs (not including depreciation): $50,000
- Depreciation method for tax purpose: 7-year MACRS
- Income tax rate: 40%.

Determine the project cash flow at the end of year 10.

(a) $69,000 (b) $73,000
(c) $66,000 (d) $67,000

Solution:

Given: accounting and financial data
Find: project cash flow at the end of year 10
Approach: use a tabular approach. Note that there will be no depreciation in year 10, as the asset will be fully depreciated in year 8.

	Year 10
Income Statement	
Revenue	$150,000
Expenses:	
O&M cost	$50,000
Depreciation	0
Taxable income	$100,000
Income taxes (40%)	$40,000
Net income	$60,000
Cash Flow Statement	
Cash flow from operation:	
Net income	$60,000
Depreciation	0
Cash flow from investing:	
Investment	
Salvage value	$15,000
Gains taxes	(6,000)
Net cash flow	$69,000

9s.3 Suppose in Problem 9s.2 the firm borrowed the entire capital investment at 10% interest over 10 years. If the required principal and interest payments in year 10 are

- Principal payment in year 10: $14,795, and
- Interest payment in year 10: $1,480,

what would be the net cash flow at the end of year 10?

(a) $46,725 (b) $63,000
(c) $62,112 (d) $53,317

Solution:

Given: accounting and financial data, with debt financing

95

Find: project cash flow at the end of year 10

Approach: use a tabular approach. Note that there will be no depreciation in year 10, as the asset will be fully depreciated in year 8. There will be entries related to financing activities.

	Year 10
Income Statement	
Revenue	$150,000
Expenses:	
O&M cost	$50,000
Depreciation	0
Debt interest	1,480
Taxable income	$98,520
Income taxes (40%)	$39,408
Net income	$59,112
Cash Flow Statement	
Cash flow from operation:	
Net income	$59,112
Depreciation	0
Cash flow from investing:	
Investment	
Salvage value	$15,000
Gains taxes	(6,000)
Cash flow from financing:	
Principal repayment	($14.795)
Net cash flow	$53,317

9s.4 Consider the following financial data for an investment project:

- Required capital investment at $n = 0$: $200,000
- Project service life: 5 years
- Salvage value at the end of 5 years: $50,000
- Depreciation method for tax purposes: 5-year MACRS
- Annual revenue: $300,000
- Annual O&M expenses (not including depreciation and interest): $180,000
- Required investment in working capital at $n = 0$ (which will be recovered in full at the end of project year): $40,000
- The income tax rate to use: 40%

Determine the project cash flow at the end of year 5.

(a) $115,088 (c) $155,824

(b) $115,824 (d) $144,304.

Solution:

<u>Given</u>: accounting and financial data

<u>Find</u>: project cash flow at the end of year 5

<u>Approach</u>: use a tabular approach. Note that there is a recovery of working capital in the amount of $40,000 at the end of year 5. There is no tax consequence on this recovery as it is not income. The book value of the asset at the end of year 5 is $23,040, so there will be gains taxes in the amount of $10,784 = ($50,000 - $23,040) × 0.40.

	Year 5
Income Statement	
Revenue	$300,000
Expenses:	
O&M cost	$180,000
Depreciation	11,520
Taxable income	$108,480
Income taxes (40%)	$43,492
Net income	$65,088
Cash Flow Statement	
Cash flow from operation:	
Net income	$65,088
Depreciation	11,520
Cash flow from investing:	
Working capital recovery	$40,000
Salvage value	$50,000
Gains taxes	(10,784)
Net cash flow	$155,824

9s.5 You are considering purchasing industrial equipment to expand one of your production lines. The equipment costs $100,000 and has an estimated service life of 6 years. Assuming that the equipment will be financed entirely from your business-retained earnings (equity funds), a fellow engineer has calculated the expected after-tax cash flows, including the salvage value, at the end of its project life are as follows:

End of Year	Net Cash Flow
0	– $100,000
1–5	500,000
6	600,000

Now you are pondering the possibility of financing the entire amount by borrowing from a local bank at 12% interest. You can make an arrangement to pay only the interest each year over the project period by deferring the principal payment until the end of 6 years. Your firm's interest rate is also 12%. The expected marginal income tax rate over the project period is known to be 40%. What is the amount of economic gain (or loss) in present worth by using debt financing over equity financing?

(a) $0   (b) $18,000

(c) $19,735   (d) $22,350.

Solution:

Given: accounting and financial data, without debt financing
Find: economic gains (losses) in present worth due to debt financing
Approach: compute the present worth of the project cash flow series with equity financing. Then determine the project cash flow series with debt financing and compute the present worth of this series. The difference in these present values is defined as the economic gains (if positive) or losses (if negative).

- Present worth of the project cash flows with 100% equity financing

$$PW(12\%) = -\$100,000 + \$500,000(P/A,12\%,6) + \$100,000(P/F,12\%,6)$$
$$= \$2,006,367$$

- Present worth of the project cash flows with 100% debt financing (Note that only the interest payments are tax deductible expenses, not the principal payment.)

n	Equity Financing	Loan Cash Flows	A/T Loan Cash Flows	Debt Financing
0	-$100,000	+$100,000	+$100,000	0
1	500,000	-12,000	-7,200	492.800
2	500,000	-12,000	-7,200	492,800

3	500,000	-12,000	-7,200	492,800
4	500,000	-12,000	-7,200	492,800
5	500,000	-12,000	-7,200	492,800
6	600,000	-112,000	-107,200	492,800
PW	**$2,006,367**			**$2,026,102**

$$PW(12\%) = \$492,800(P/A,12\%,6)$$
$$= \$2,026,102$$

- Gains (or losses) due to debt financing

$$\Delta = \$2,026,102 - \$2,006,367 = \$19,735$$

9s.6 A corporation is considering purchasing a machine that will save $130,000 per year before taxes. The cost of operating the machine, including maintenance, is $20,000 per year. The machine will be needed for 4 years, after which it will have a zero salvage value. MACRS depreciation will be used assuming a 3-year class. The allowed depreciation amount as a percentage of the initial cost will be 33.33%, 44.45%, 14.81%, and 7.41%, respectively. If the firm wants a 12% rate of return after taxes, how much can it afford to pay for this machine? The firm's income tax rate is 40%.

(a) $295,584 (b) $350,800
(c) $400,750 (d) $435,245.

Solution:

Given: accounting and financial data
Find: the size of investment (X)
Approach: Instead of using the income statement approach, we may use an analytical approach.

- Present worth of cash inflows

$$PW(12\%)_{\text{Revenue}} = \$130,000(1 - 0.40)(P/A,12\%,4) = \$236,913$$

$$PW(12\%)_{\text{Depreciation credit}} = 0.40X[0.3333(P/F,12\%,1) + 0.4445(P/F,12\%,2)$$
$$+0.1481(P/F,12\%,3) + 0.0741(P/F,12\%,4)]$$
$$= 0.40X(0.8044) = 0.3218X$$

$$PW(12\%)_{\text{Inflows}} = \$236,913 + 0.3218X$$

- Present worth of cash outflow

$$PW(12\%)_{\text{Outflows}} = X + \$20,000(1 - 0.40)(P/A, 12\%, 4) = \$36,448 + X$$

- Required investment to breakeven

$$236,913 + 0.3218X = 36,448 + X$$
$$0.6782X = 200,465$$
$$X = \$295,584$$

9s.7 You are planning to lease an automobile for 36 months from an auto dealer. The negotiated price is $20,000. The required security deposit is $500 at the time of the lease and will be refunded in full at the end of the lease. The monthly lease payment at the end of each month is calculated to be $300. What kind of residual value (salvage value) was assumed by the dealer in calculating the monthly lease? The dealer's interest rate is known to be 9%, compounded monthly.

(a) $9,200   (c) $13,674

(b) $12,124   (d) $14,481

Solution:

Given: $I = \$20,000$, monthly lease payment = $300, refundable security deposit = $500, $r = 9\%$ compounded monthly, $N = 36$ months

Find: the residual value of the automobile assumed at the end of 36 months

Approach: use the capital recovery with return formula

- PW of total revenue from leasing
  $$\$300(P/A, 0.75\%, 36) = \$9,434$$
- PW of total investment by the lesser
  $$\$20,000 - \$500 - (S - 500)(P/F, 0.75\%, 36) = -0.7641S + 19,882$$
- Assumed residual value (S)

$$-0.7641S + 19,882 = 9,434$$
$$S = \$13,674$$

9s.8 A corporation is considering purchasing a machine that costs $120,000 and will save $X per year after taxes. The cost of operating the machine, including maintenance and depreciation, is $20,000 per year after taxes. The machine will be needed for 4 years, after which it will have a zero salvage value. If the firm wants a 14% rate of return after taxes, what is the minimum after tax annual savings that must be generated to realize a 14% rate of return after taxes?

(a) $50,000   (c) $91,974

(b) $61,184   (d) $101,974

Solution:

Given: $I = \$120,000$, $S = 0$, O&M = $20,000 per year, $N = 4$ years, MARR = 14%

Find: required annual savings (X)

Approach: Set up a present worth equation as a function of X.

$$PW(14\%) = -\$120,000 + (X - 20,000)(P/A, 14\%, 4)$$
$$= -\$120,000 + 2.9137X - \$58,274 = 0$$
$$2.9137X = \$178,274$$
$$X = \$61,284$$

9s.9 Cutter Ltd. is planning to invest $150,000 in an automated screw-cutting machine to enhance its current operations. Due to a lack of internal funds, its management is planning to borrow 60% of the investment from a local bank at an interest rate of 10% payable in 5 equal payments. What is the principal payment in year 2 that should be included in the cash flow analysis?

(a) $7,526   (c) $9,000

(b) $16,216   (d) $23,742

Solution:

Given: $i = 10\%$, debt ratio = 0.6, amount of borrowing = $90,000. $N = 5$ years

Find: the principal amount in the 2nd payment

Approach: develop a loan payment schedule. First determine the annual loan payment amount, $A = \$90,000(A/P, 10\%, 5) = \$23,742$

	0	1	2
Beg. Balance		$90,000	$75,258
Interest (10%)		$9,000	$7,526
Payment		$23,742	$23,742
Ending Balance	$90,000	$75,258	$59,042
Principal Payment	0	$14,742	$16,216

9s.10 A corporation is considering purchasing a machine that will save $200,000 per year before taxes. The cost of operating the machine, including maintenance, is $80,000 per year. The machine costing $150,000 will be needed for 5 years, after which it will have a salvage value of $25,000. A straight-line depreciation with no half-year convention applies (i.e., 20% each year). If the firm wants 15% rate of return after taxes, what is the net present value of the cash flows generated from this machine? The firm's income tax rate is 40%.

(a) $165,600   (c) $199,460
(b) $218,313   (d) $375,000

Solution:

Given: financial data, MARR = 15%, t_m = 40%
Find: net present value of the project
Approach: Obtain the after tax cash flow series using the income statement approach

	0	1	2	3	4	5
Income Statement						
Revenue		$200	$200	$200	$200	$200
Expenses:						
O&M		80	80	80	80	80
Depreciation		30	30	30	30	30
Taxable income		120	120	120	120	120
Income taxes (40%)		48	48	48	48	48
Net income		$72	$72	$72	$72	$72
Cash Flow Statement						
Cash flow from operation:						
Net income		$72	$72	$72	$72	$72
Depreciation		30	30	30	30	30
Cash flow from investing:						
Investment	($150)					
Salvage value						25
Gains taxes						(10)
Net cash flow	-$150	$102	$102	$102	$102	$117

$$PW(15\%) = -\$150 + \$102(P/A, 15\%, 5) + \$15(P/F, 15\%, 5) = \$199.46$$

9s.11 Oxford Manufacturing Company needs an air compressor and has narrowed the choice to two alternatives, A and B. The following financial data have been collected:

	Model A	Model B
First cost	$25,000	$35,000
Annual O&M cost	5,600	3,500
Salvage value	0	4,000
Service life	10 years	10 years
Depreciation	5-year MACRS	5-year MACRS

The marginal tax rate is 40%. Which of the following statements is incorrect? Assume the MARR = 20%.

(a) Select Model A because you can save $440 annua lly.

(b) Select Model A because its incremental rate of return (Model A – Model B) exceeds 20%.

(c) Select Model A because you can save $1,845 in present worth.

(d) Select Model A because its incremental rate of return (Model B – Model A) is 14.12%, which is less than 20%.

Solution:

Given: financial data for two mutually exclusive alternatives
Find: the correct statement
Approach: compute the after cash flows for each alternative and perform an incremental analysis

Model A

n	Investment	O&M	Depreciation	Taxable Income	Income Taxes	Net A/T Cash Flow
0	$ (25,000)					$ (25,000)
1		$ (5,600)	$ (5,000)	$ (10,600)	$ (4,240)	$ (1,360)
2		$ (5,600)	$ (8,000)	$ (13,600)	$ (5,440)	$ (160)
3		$ (5,600)	$ (4,800)	$ (10,400)	$ (4,160)	$ (1,440)
4		$ (5,600)	$ (2,880)	$ (8,480)	$ (3,392)	$ (2,208)
5		$ (5,600)	$ (2,880)	$ (8,480)	$ (3,392)	$ (2,208)
6		$ (5,600)	$ (1,440)	$ (7,040)	$ (2,816)	$ (2,784)
7		$ (5,600)		$ (5,600)	$ (2,240)	$ (3,360)
8		$ (5,600)		$ (5,600)	$ (2,240)	$ (3,360)
9		$ (5,600)		$ (5,600)	$ (2,240)	$ (3,360)
10		$ (5,600)		$ (5,600)	$ (2,240)	$ (3,360)

Model B

n	Investment	O&M	Depreciation	Taxable Income	Income Taxes	Net A/T Cash Flow
0	$ (35,000)					$ (35,000)
1		$ (3,500)	$ (7,000)	$ (10,500)	$ (4,200)	$ 700
2		$ (3,500)	$ (11,200)	$ (14,700)	$ (5,880)	$ 2,380
3		$ (3,500)	$ (6,720)	$ (10,220)	$ (4,088)	$ 588
4		$ (3,500)	$ (4,032)	$ (7,532)	$ (3,013)	$ (487)
5		$ (3,500)	$ (4,032)	$ (7,532)	$ (3,013)	$ (487)
6		$ (3,500)	$ (2,016)	$ (5,516)	$ (2,206)	$ (1,294)
7		$ (3,500)		$ (3,500)	$ (1,400)	$ (2,100)
8		$ (3,500)		$ (3,500)	$ (1,400)	$ (2,100)
9		$ (3,500)		$ (3,500)	$ (1,400)	$ (2,100)
10	$ 4,000	$ (3,500)		$ (3,500)	$ (1,400)	$ 300

n	Model A	Model B	Incremental B - A
0	$ (25,000)	$ (35,000)	$ (10,000)
1	$ (1,360)	$ 700	$ 2,060
2	$ (160)	$ 2,380	$ 2,540
3	$ (1,440)	$ 588	$ 2,028
4	$ (2,208)	$ (487)	$ 1,721
5	$ (2,208)	$ (487)	$ 1,721
6	$ (2,784)	$ (1,294)	$ 1,490
7	$ (3,360)	$ (2,100)	$ 1,260
8	$ (3,360)	$ (2,100)	$ 1,260
9	$ (3,360)	$ (2,100)	$ 1,260
10	$ (3,360)	$ 300	$ 3,660

PW(20%) = $ (1,845)

AE(20%) = $ (440)

IRR(B-A) = 14.11%

The correct answer is (b).

9s.12 Which of the following statements is <u>incorrect</u> under inflationary economy?

    (a) Borrowers will always come out ahead as they pay back with cheaper dollars.

    (b) In general, you will pay more taxes in real dollars if you have depreciable assets.

    (c) In general, there will be more drain in working capital.

    (d) Bond interest rates will tend to be higher in the financial market, so that it would cost more to finance a new project.

Solution:

    <u>Given</u>: statements under inflationary environment
    <u>Find</u>: the incorrect statement

    The correct answer is (a). Under the inflationary economy, lenders will normally charge a higher interest rate to protect them from loss in purchasing power.

9s.13 Vermont Casting has received an order to supply 250 units of casted fireplace inserts each year for Midwestern Builders over a 2-year period. The current sales price is $1,500 per unit, and the current cost per unit is $1,000. Vermont is taxed at a rate of 40%. Both prices and costs are expected to rise at a rate of 6% per year. Vermont will produce these units on fully-depreciated existing machines. Since the orders will be filled at the end of each year, the unit sale price and unit cost during the first year would be $1,590 and $1,060, respectively. Vermont's market interest rate is 15%. Which of the following net present worth calculation is <u>incorrect</u>?

    (a) PW = $500(1 - 0.4)(P/F, 8.49%, 1) $\div$ $561.8(1 - 0.40)(P/F, 15%, 2)

    (b) PW = $530(1 - 0.4)[(P/F, 15%, 1) $\div$ (1.06)(P/F, 15%, 2)]

    (c) PW = $500(1 - 0.4)(P/A, 9%, 2)

    (d) PW = $500(1 - 0.4)(P/A, 8.49%, 2).

Solution:

    <u>Given</u>: statements under inflationary environment
    <u>Find</u>: the incorrect statement
    <u>Approach</u>: Project cash flows may be stated in one of two forms: (1) actual dollars and (2) constant dollars. Then, use the market interest rate to calculate the present worth of actual dollars. For constant dollars, use the inflation-free interest rate. In our example, the market interest rate is 15% and the inflation rate is 6%. The inflation-free interest rate can be calculated as 8.49%.

- (a) is correct, as the first year cash flow is expressed in constant dollars whereas the second year cash flow is expressed in actual dollars.
- (b) is also correct, as all cash flows expressed in actual dollars and the market interest rate is used to find the present worth of the project.
- (c) is incorrect, as the precise inflation-free interest rate is 8.49%.
- (d) is correct.

9s.14 The North Dakota Mining Company has the following capital structure.

Source	Amount
Debt	$665,000
Equity	1,545,000

The company wants to maintain the current capital structure in future project financing. If the company is allowed to use $800,000 debt, what would be the scale of the total investment?

(a) $1,144,337   (b) $2,658,647

(c) $1,333,334   (d) $2,456,785

Solution:

<u>Given</u>: capital structure, debt limit = $800,000

<u>Find</u>: amount of total investment

<u>Approach</u>: find the debt to equity ratio, and then calculate the amount of equity to raise

$$\text{debt to equity ratio} = \frac{\$665,000}{\$2,210,000} = 30\%$$

$$\$665,000 : \$1,545,000 = \$800,000 : X$$

$$X = \$1,858,647$$

Total investment = $800,000 + $1,858,647 = $2,658,647

9s.15 Delta Corporation needs to raise $10 million for plant modernization. Delta's target capital structure calls for a debt ratio of 0.4, indicating that $6 million has to be financed from equity.

- Delta's beta (ß) is known to be 1.4, which is greater than 1, indicating the firm is perceived more risky than market average.

- The risk free interest rate is 6%, and the average market return is 13% (all these interest rates are adjusted to reflect inflation in the economy).

106

Determine the cost of equity to finance the plant modernization.

(a) 6%   (b) 7.00%

(c) 13.0%   (d) 15.80%

Solution:

Given: debt ratio = 0.40, the amount of equity to raise = $6 million, β = 1.4, r_f = 6%, r_M = 13%

Find: cost of equity, i_e

Approach: use the cost of equity formula given in Eq. (9.1)

$$i_e = r_f + \beta[r_M - r_f]$$
$$= 0.06 + 1.4[0.13 - 0.06]$$
$$= 15.80\%$$

9s.16 In 9s.15, to finance the remaining portion of the project ($4 million), a $1,000 par value bond with a coupon rate of 10% will be issued. However the effective debt interest rate considering the cost of issuing the bond (commonly known as floatation cost) is 10.75%. Delta's corporate tax rate is 38%. Compute the after-tax cost of this debt financing.

(a) 10%   (b) 10.75%

(c) 6.67%   (d) 6%.

Solution:

Given: debt ratio = 0.40, the amount of debt to raise = $4 million, k_b = 10.75%, t_m = 38%,

Find: cost of debt, i_d

Approach: use the cost of debt formula given in Eq. (9.2). Since there is no term loan, the entire amount will be raised by issuing bond.

$$i_d = (1 - 0.38)10.75\%$$
$$= 6.67\%$$

9s.17 The capital structure for Florida Citrus Corporation is given as follows:

Capital Structure

Sources	Amount
ng term bonds	$3,000,000
Common stock	7,000,000

Assuming that the firm will maintain its capital structure in the future, determine the firm's weighted average cost of capital (k) if the firm has a 7.5% cost of debt (after-tax) and a 20% cost of common stock (cost of equity).

(a) 13.43%   (b) 16.25%

(c) 13.75%   (d) 19.33%.

Solution:

Given: debt ratio $= 0.30$, $i_d = 7.5\%$, $i_e = 20\%$

Find: weighted average cost of capital, k

Approach: use the cost of capital formula given in Eq. (9.3).

$$k = (0.3)(0.075) + (0.70)(0.20) = 16.25\%$$

9s.18 The Fox Corporation is considering three investments. The required investments and expected IRRs of these projects are as follows:

Investment Opportunity Schedule

Project	Investment	IRR
A	$180,000	32%
B	250,000	18
C	120,000	15

The company intends to finance the projects by 40% debt and 60% equity. The after-tax cost of debt is 8% for the first $100,000, after which the cost will be 10%. Retained earnings (internally generated) in the amount of $150,000 are available for investment. The common stockholders' required rate of return is 20%. If new stock is issued, the cost will be 23%. What would be the marginal cost of capital to raise the first $250,000 project cost?

108

(a) 15.2%   (b) 17.8%

(c) 16.5%   (d) 8%.

Solution:

Given: debt ratio = 0.40, i_d = 8% for the first $100,000, 10% over $100,000, i_e = 20% up to $150,000, 23% over $150,000

Find: marginal cost of capital, k, to raise $250,000

Approach: use the cost of capital formula given in Eq. (9.3).

- Amount of debt financing and its cost

$$(0.40)(\$250,000) = \$100,000$$

$$i_d = 8\%$$

- Amount of equity financing and its cost

$$(0.60)(\$250,000) = \$150,000$$

$$i_e = 20\%$$

- Marginal cost of capital to raise $250,000

$$k = (0.40)(0.08) + (0.60)(0.20) = 15.20\%$$

9s.19 Using the marginal cost of capital curve defined in Problem 9s.18, decide which project(s) would be included, if there is no limit on budget.

(a) Project A only

(b) Projects A and B

(c) Projects A, B, and C

(d) None of the projects.

Solution:

Given: debt ratio = 0.40, i_d = 8% for the first $100,000, 10% over $100,000, i_e = 20% up to $150,000, 23% over $150,000

Find: marginal cost of capital, k, to raise $250,000

Approach: use the cost of capital formula given in Eq. (9.3).

- To accept Project C, we need to raise $120,000, which will cost 15.20%. However, IRR_C is only 12%, so Project C will not be considered.
- To accept Project B, we need to raise $150,000, which will cost 15.20%. Since IRR_B > 15.20%, so we accept Project B.
- To accept Project A, we need to raise $180,000, which cost 15.20%. Since IRR_A > 15.20%, so we can accept Project A as well.

- If we were to consider both A and B, we need to raise $430,000. The marginal cost of capital financing up to $150,000 is 15.2%, so any amount above this limit will raise the marginal cost of capital, which is

$$k = (0.40)(0.10) + (0.60)(0.23) = 17.8\%$$

Technically, we will accept Project A first at $k = 15.20\%$. It will use up $120,000. To consider Project B, we need to raise $250,000. We can still raise $130,000 of $250,000 at $k = 15.20\%$, but the remaining balance has to be at $k = 17.80\%$. The combined weighted average of this financing will be 16.45%. Since $IRR_B > 16.45\%$, we can go ahead and accept Project B as well.

Chapter 10 Handling Project Uncertainty

10s.1 For a certain investment project, the net present worth can be expressed as functions of sales price (X) and variable production cost Y of PW = $10,450(2X - Y) - 7890$. The base values for X and Y are $20 and $10, respectively. If the sales price is increased 10% over the base price, how much change in NPW can be expected?

(a) 10%   (b) 20%

(c) 13.68%   (d) 22.32%.

Solution:

Given: PW expression as a function of sales price (X) and variable production cost (Y)

Find: percent change in PW (or ΔPW) when X is increased by 10%

$$X = \$20 \quad X \rightarrow \$22 \text{ (or } \Delta = \$2)$$

$$Y = \$10$$

$$PW_{base} = 10,450(2\times 20 - 10) - 7890 = \$305,610$$

$$PW_{\Delta=10\%} = 10,450(2\times 22 - 10) - 7890 = \$347,410$$

$$\Delta = \frac{347,410 - 305,610}{305,610} = 13.68\%$$

10s.2 An investor bought 100 shares of stock at a cost of $10 per share. He held the stock for 15 years and wants to sell it now. For the first 3 years, he received no dividends. For each of the next 7 years, he received total dividends of $100 per year. For each of the remaining 5 years, no dividends were paid. In the last 15 years, the investor's marginal tax rate and capital gain tax rate was averaging about 30% and 20%, respectively. What would be the break-even selling price to earn a 15% return on investment after-tax?

(a) $6,579   (b) $7,977

(c) $8,224   (d) $9,398.

Solution:

Given: $I = \$1,000$, $= 15$ years, $t_m = 30\%$, gains tax rate $= 20\%$, cash dividend $= (0,0,0,\$100,100,100,100,100,100,100,0,0,0,0,0)$, required return $= 15\%$

Find: breakeven selling price (F)

111

Approach: express the present value of the investment as a function of selling price

$$PW(15\%) = -\$1,000 + \$100(1-0.30)(P/A,15\%,7)(P/F,15\%,3)$$
$$+ \left[X - (X - 1,000)0.2\right](P/F,15\%,5)$$
$$= -\$1,000 + \$191.49 + 0.0983X + \$24.58$$
$$= 0$$
$$0.0983X = \$784.12$$
$$X = \$7,977$$

10s.3 A company is currently paying a sales representative $0.25 per mile to drive her car for company business. The company is considering supplying the representative with a car, which would involve the following: A car costs $12,000, has a service life of 5 years, and a market value of $3,500 at the end of that time. Monthly storage costs for the car are $80, and the cost of fuel, tires, and maintenance is 15 cents per mile. The car will be depreciated by MACRS, using a recovery period of 5 years (20%, 32%, 19.20%, 11.52%, 11.52%). The firm's marginal tax rate is 40%. What annual mileage must a salesman travel by car for the cost of the two methods of providing transportation to be equal if the interest rate is 15%?

(a) 36,345 miles (b) 41,235 miles
(c) 45,233 miles (d) 47,518 miles

Solution:

Given: financial data for both options
Find: number of miles to be driven to breakeven (X)
Approach: find the total present value of each option as a function of a decision variable (number of miles to be driven, X)
- Option 1: Reimbursement plan

$$PW(15\%)_{\text{Option 1}} = 0.25X(1-0.40)(P/A,15\%,5) = 0.5028X$$

- Option 2: Plan for owning and operating a vehicle

$$PW(15\%)_{\text{Option 2}} = \$12,000 + (960 + 0.15X)(1 - 0.4)(P/A,15\%,5)$$
$$-0.4(\$12,000)[0.20(P/F,15\%,1) + 0.32(P/F,15\%,2)$$
$$+0.1920(P/F,15\%,3) + 0.1152(P/F,15\%,4)$$
$$+(0.5)(0.1152)(P/F,15\%,5)]$$
$$-[\$3,500 - (\$3,500 - \$1,382)(0.4)](P/F,15\%,5)$$
$$= \$9,556 + 0.3017X$$

- Breakeven value (X)

$$0.5028X = \$9,556 + 0.3017X$$
$$X = 47,518 \text{ miles}$$

10s.4 Project A has the following probability distribution of expected future returns:

Probability	Net Future Worth
0.1	-$12,000
0.2	4,000
0.4	12,000
0.2	20,000
0.1	30,000

What is the expected future worth for Project A?

(a) $9,450   (b) $10,800
(c) $11,400   (d) $12,300

Solution:

Given: probabilistic events and associated probabilities
Find: the expected FW
$$E[FW] = -\$12,000(0.1) + \$4,000(0.2) + \$12,000(0.4)$$
$$+\$20,000(0.2) + \$30,000(0.1)$$
$$= \$11,400$$

10s.5 In Problem 10s.4, what is the standard deviation of expected future worth for Project A?

(a) $10,735   (b) $3,686
(c) $11,400   (d) $2,280

Solution:

Given: data as in 10s.4
Find: standard deviation of FW

$$V[PW] = (-12,000 - 11,400)^2 (0.1) + (4,000 - 11,400)^2 (0.2)$$
$$+ (12,000 - 11,400)^2 (0.4) + (20,000 - 11,400)^2 (0.2)$$
$$+ (30,000 - 11,400)^2 (0.1)$$
$$= 115,240,000$$
$$\sigma[FW] = \sqrt{115,240,000} = \$10,735$$

10s.6 In a resort location, you find a slot machine that costs you $1.00 per play. Odds for potential payoffs are as follows:

With 100 plays, what is the expected value of net payoff?

Payoff	Probability
$25	0.01
$1	0.50
$0	0.49

(a) -$25   (b) $0
(c) $25   (d) $75

Solution:

Given: pay-off table, number of trials = 100
Find: the expected pay-off after 100 trials
Approach: compute the expected pay-off per trial and multiply this number by the number of total trails

$$E[\text{pay off}] = 100[\$25(0.01) + \$1(0.50) + \$0(0.49) - \$1]$$
$$= -\$25$$

You are expected to lose $25 if you try 100 times.

10s.7 The Arizona Mining contemplates investing $4 million in new sets of ripping equipment to expand its copper mining operation. The management of the company forecasts that the new investment will generate incremental net cash inflows of A_i (i =1, 2, ..., 5) where each of the A_i is a random variable with a mean of $2 million and a standard deviation of $400,000. The salvage value of the mining equipment at the end of year 5 will be also a random variable with a mean of $1 million and a standard deviation of $300,000. Compute the mean and variance of the present value of this investment. Assume that the cash inflows of A_i are mutually independent random variables and the risk-free interest rate is 10%.

Solution:

> Given: $I = \$4$ million, $A_i = (\mu: \$2$ million, $\sigma: \$0.4$ million), $S = (\mu: \$1$ million, $\sigma: \$0.3$ million), $N = 5$ years, $r = 10\%$
>
> Find: mean and variance of the present value of the project
>
> Approach: Use Eqs. (10.1) and (10.2)

$$E[PW(10\%)] = -\$4 + \$2(P/A, 10\%, 5) + \$1(P/F, 10\%, 5)$$
$$= \$2.9607$$

$$V[PW(10\%)] = \frac{0.4^2}{(1+0.10)^2} + \frac{0.4^2}{(1+0.10)^4} + \frac{0.4^2}{(1+0.10)^6} + \frac{0.4^2}{(1+0.10)^8} + \frac{0.4^2+0.3^2}{(1+0.10)^{10}}$$
$$= 0.4^2(P/A, 21\%, 5) + 0.3^2(P/F, 21\%, 5)$$
$$= 0.2220$$

$$\sigma = \sqrt{0.2220} = \$0.4711$$

10s.8 In 10s.7, the degree of project cash flow uncertainty is rather captured by adjusting the discount rate from 10% to 15%. Determine the certainty equivalent present value of the project at this risk-adjusted discount rate.

Solution:

> Given: $I = \$4$ million, $A_i = (\mu: \$2$ million, $\sigma: \$0.4$ million), $S = (\mu: \$1$ million, $\sigma: \$0.3$ million), $N = 5$ years, $i = 15\%$
>
> Find: mean and variance of the present value of the project
>
> Approach: find the certainty equivalent value at $i = 15\%$

$$PW(15\%) = -\$4 + \$2(P/A, 15\%, 5) + \$1(P/F, 15\%, 5)$$
$$= \$3.2015$$

The project is still profitable at a higher discount rate.

10s.9 Harry Wilson, a mechanical engineer at Lehigh manufacturing, has found that the anticipated profitability of a newly developed motion detector for its popular home security device product line can be estimated as follows:

$$PW = 40.28\,W(2X - 11) - 77,860$$

where W is the number of units produced and sold, and X is the sales price per unit. Harry also found that W parameter value could occur anywhere over a range of 1,000 to 6,000 units and the X parameter value anywhere between \$20 and \$40 per unit.

Suppose both W and X are statistically independent continuous random variables with the following means and variances:

$$E[W] = 3,500, \ V[W] = 2,083,333$$
$$E[X] = 30, \ V[X] = 33.$$

What is the variance of PW?

(a) 2.2309×10^{11}

(b) 4.4618×10^{11}

(c) 2.769×10^{9}

(d) 1.118549×10^{13}.

Solution:

Given: PW expression as a function W and X
Find: V[PW]
Approach: Let $Y = (2X - 11)$. Then, $E[Y] = E[2X - 11] = 2E[X] - 11 = 49$, $V[Y] = V[2X - 11] = 2^2 V[X] = 4(33) = 132$. Now the PW expression can be a function of W and Y. It requires understanding the variance operation for a product of random variables.

- Mean of PW

$$V[Y] = V[2X - 11] = 2^2 V[X] = 4(33) = 132$$
$$E[PW] = E[40.28WY - 77,860]$$
$$= 40.28 E[W]E[Y] - 77,860$$
$$= \$6,830,160$$

- Variance of PW

$$V[PW] = V[40.28WY - 77,860]$$
$$= 40.28^2 V[WY]$$
$$= 40.28^2 E\left\{[WY - E(WY)]^2\right\}$$
$$= 40.28^2 E[(WY)^2] - [E(WY)]^2$$
$$= 40.28^2 \left\{E(W^2)E(Y^2) - [E(W)E(Y)]^2\right\}$$

Knowing that $E(W^2) = V[W] + \{E[W]\}^2$ and $E(Y^2) = V[Y] + \{E[Y]\}^2$

$$V[PW] = 40.28^2 \left\{[E(W)]^2 V[Y] + [E(Y)]^2 V[W] + V[W]V[Y]\right\}$$
$$= 40.28^2 \left\{(3500)^2(132) + (49)^2(2,083,333) + (2,083,333)(132)\right\}$$
$$= 40.28^2 (6,894,082,489)$$
$$= 1.118549 \times 10^{13}$$
$$\sigma[PW] = \$3,344,473$$

10s.10 In 10s.9, if V and X are mutually independent discrete random variables with the following probabilities:

V		X	
Event	Probability	Event	Probability
1,000	0.4	$20	0.7
6,000	0.6	$40	0.3

What is the probability that the PW would exceed $6,000,000?

(a)   0.28   (c) 0.60
(b)   0.40   (d) 0.82.

Solution:

Given: PW expression given in 10s.9
Find: the probability that PW will exceed $6,000,000
Approach: develop a PW distribution by enumerating all possible joint events and the PWs associated with these joint events.

Event	(W,X)	Joint Probabilities	PW = 40.28W(2X - 11) – 77,860
1	(1000,20)	(0.4)(0.7) = 0.28	$1,090,260
2	(1000,40)	(0.4)(0.3) = 0.12	$2,701,460
3	(6000,20)	(0.6)(0.7) = 0.42	$6,930,860
4	(6000,40)	(0.6)(0.3) = 0.18	$16,598,060
		Σ = 1.00	E[PW] = $6,528,060

The probability that PW will exceed $6,000,000 is 0.60 (=0.42 + 0.18). In other words, only Events 3 and 4 will satisfy the statement.

Chapter 11 Replacement Decisions

Problem Statement for Questions (11s.1–11s.5)

A machine now in use, which was bought 5 years ago for $4,000, has been fully depreciated. It can be sold for $2,500, but could be used for 3 more years (remaining useful life), at the end of which time it would have no salvage value. The annual operating and maintenance costs for the old machine amount to $10,000. A new machine can be purchased at an invoice price of $14,000 to replace the present equipment. Because of the nature of the manufactured product, the new machine has an expected economic life of 3 years, and it will have no salvage value at the end of that time. The new machine's expected operating and maintenance costs amount to $2,000 for the first year and $3,000 for each of the next 2 years. The income tax rate is 34%. Any gains will aso be taxed at 34%. The allowed depreciation amounts for the new machine are $1,400 during the first year, and $2,800 per year for the next 2 years. The firm's interest rate is 15%.

11s.1 If the old machine is to be sold now, what will be the gains tax?

(a) $800   (b) $850

(c) $900   (d) $950.

Solution:

    Given: fully depreciated asset, current market value = $2,500
    Find: gains tax

$$\text{gains tax} = (\text{Salvage value - Book value})(\text{tax rate})$$
$$= (\$2,500 - \$0)((34\%) = \$850$$

11s.2 If you decide to retain the old machine for now, what will be the opportunity cost?

(a) $2,500   (b) $4,000

(c) $1,650   (d) $1,500.

Solution:

    Given: fully depreciated asset, current market value = $2,500
    Find: opportunity cost of retaining the old machine

$$\text{Opportunity cost} = \text{Net proceeds from sales of old asset}$$
$$= \$2,500 - \$850 = \$1,650$$

11s.3 If the old asset is to be sold now, its sunk cost is

(a) $2,500   (b) $4,000

(c) $1,650   (d) $1,500.

Solution:

Given: fully depreciated asset, current market value = $2,500
Find: sunk cost associated with the old asset

$$\text{Sunk cost} = (\text{Initial cost - current market value})$$
$$=(\$4,000 - \$2,500)$$
$$=\$1,500$$

11s.4 For depreciation purposes, the first cost of the new machine under the opportunity cost approach will be

(a) $14,000   (b) $11,500

(c) $12,350   (d) $16,500.

Solution:

Given: fully depreciated asset, current market value = $2,500
Find: depreciation base for the challenger

- Cash flow approach:
    First cost for challenger = New invoice for challenger – Net proceeds from
    Sales of old asset
    = $14,000 - $1,650
    =$12,350
- Opportunity cost approach:
    First cost for challenger = Invoice price = $14,000

11s.5 What is the incremental annual after-tax benefit of replacing the old machine?

(a) $809   (b) $919

(c) $967   (d) $992.

Solution:

Given: financial and accounting data as provided above, $i = 15\%$
Find: incremental annual after-tax benefit of replacing the old asset

<u>Approach</u>: develop an after-tax cash flow series for each alternative, and then compute the annual equivalent cost for each alternative. The difference in these AE values (Challenger – Defender) is the incremental benefits for replacing the old the asset. Note that the book value of the challenger at the end of year 3 will be $7,000, indicating a book loss in the amount of $7,000 (= $14,000 - $7,000). The tax credit on this loss is (0.34)($7,000) = $2,380.

	Defender			Challenger		
	Market value	Dep.	O&M	Market value	Dep.	O&M
0	$2,500			$14,000		
1		0	10,000		$1,400	$2,000
2		0	10,000		$2,800	3,000
3	0	0	10,000	0	$2,800	3,000

- Defender

$$PW(15\%)_{\text{Defender}} = (1-0.34)(\$2,500) + (1-0.34)(10,000)(P/A,15\%,3)$$
$$= \$1,650 + \$15,069 = \$16,719$$
$$AE(15\%)_{\text{Defender}} = \$16,719(A/P,15\%,3) = \$7,323$$

- Challenger

$$PW(15\%)_{\text{Challenger}} = \$14,000 + (1-0.34)[\$2,000(P/F,15\%,1)$$
$$+\$3,000(P/A,15\%,2)(P/F,15\%,1)]$$
$$-0.34[\$1,400(P/F,15\%,1) + \$2,800(P/A,15\%,2)(P/F,15\%,1)]$$
$$-0.34(14,000 - \$7,000)(P/F,15\%,3)$$
$$= \$14,000 + \$3,947 - \$1,760 - \$1,565$$
$$= \$14,622$$
$$AE(15\%)_{\text{Challenger}} = \$14,622(A/P,15\%,3) = \$6,404$$

- Challenger – Defender

$$AE(15\%)_{\text{Challenger}} - AE(15\%)_{\text{Defender}} = \$6,404 - \$7,323$$
$$= -\$919 \text{ (or benefits)}$$

11s.6 A local delivery company has purchased a delivery truck for $15,000. The truck will be depreciated under the MACRS as a 5-year property (for a 5-year property, the MACRS percentages are 20%, 32%, 19.2%, 11.52%, 11.52%, 5.76%). The truck's market value (or selling price) is expected to be $2,500 less each year. The O&M costs are expected to be $3,000 per year. The firm is in a 40% tax bracket, and its MARR is 15%. Compute the annual equivalent cost for retaining the truck for a 2-year period, which will be

(a) $5,527   (b) $5,175

(c) $5,362   (d) $5,014.

Solution:

Given: $I = \$15,000$, $S_n = \$15,000 - \$2,500n$, depreciation method = 5 year MACRS, O&M cost = $3,000 per year, $t_m = 40\%$, MARR = 15%

Find: annual equivalent cost for keeping the truck for 2 years

n	Market Value (S_n)	Depreciation	O&M
0	$15,000		
1	12,500	$3,000	$3,000
2	10,000	4,800	3,000
3	7,500	2,880	3,000
4	2,500	1,728	3,000
5	0	1,728	3,000
6	0	864	3,000

$$PW(15\%)_{N = 2 \text{ years}} = \$15,000$$
$$+(1-0.40)(\$3,000)(P/A,15\%,2)$$
$$-0.40[\$3,000(P/F,15\%,1)+(0.5)(\$4,800)(P/F,15\%,2)]$$
$$-[\$10,000-(\$10,000-\$9,600)(0.40)](P/F,15\%,2)$$
$$= \$8,717$$
$$AE(15\%)_{N = 2 \text{ years}} = \$8,717(A/P,15\%,2)$$
$$= \$5,362$$

Note that the book value of the asset at the end of year 2 is $9,600. There will be taxable gains in the amount of $400.

11s.7 The following table summarizes the financial data for a proposed new asset. The issue is how long the asset should be kept. Assume an interest rate of 12% and determine the economic service life of the asset before taxes.

End of Year (n)	Investment Cost	O&M Cost	Salvage Value
0	$14,000		
1		$3,400	$8,000
2		4,600	6,000
3		5,800	4,000
4		7,200	2,000
5		8.300	0

(a) 2 years   (b) 3 years
(c) 4 years   (d) 5 years

Solution:

Given: financial data above and MARR = 12%
Find: economic service life based on before taxes

$$AE(12\%)_{n=1} = (\$14,000 - \$8,000)(A/P,12\%,1) + 0.12(\$8,000)$$
$$+\$3,400$$
$$= \$11,080$$

$$AE(12\%)_{n=2} = (\$14,000 - \$6,000)(A/P,12\%,2) + 0.12(\$6,000)$$
$$+[\$3,400(P/F,12\%,1) + \$4,600(P/F,12\%,2)](A/P,12\%,2)$$
$$= \$9,420$$

$$AE(12\%)_{n=3} = (\$14,000 - \$4,000)(A/P,12\%,3) + 0.12(\$4,000)$$
$$+[\$3,400(P/F,12\%,1) + \$4,600(P/F,12\%,2)$$
$$+\$5,800(P/F,12\%,3)](A/P,12\%,3)$$
$$= \$9,153$$

$$AE(12\%)_{n=4} = (\$14,000 - \$2,000)(A/P,12\%,4) + 0.12(\$2,000)$$
$$+[\$3,400(P/F,12\%,1) + \$4,600(P/F,12\%,2)$$
$$+\$5,800(P/F,12\%,3) + \$7,200(P/F,12\%,4)](A/P,12\%,4)$$
$$= \$9,263$$

$$AE(12\%)_{n=5} = (\$14,000)(A/P,12\%,4)$$
$$+[\$3,400(P/F,12\%,1) + \$4,600(P/F,12\%,2)$$
$$+\$5,800(P/F,12\%,3) + \$7,200(P/F,12\%,4)$$
$$+\$8,300(P/F,12\%,5)](A/P,12\%,5)$$
$$= \$9,464$$

The economic service life is 3 years.

11s.8 The annual equivalent after-tax costs of retaining a defender over its 3-year remaining life and the annual equivalent operating costs for its challenger over its 4-year physical life are as follows:

Holding	Annual Equivalent Cost	
Period	Defender	Challenger
1	$3,000	$5,000
2	2,500	4,000
3	3,200	3,100
4		4,500

Assume a MARR of 12% and determine the optimal replacement time for the defender. Assume an infinite planning horizon and no technological change (cost) in the challenger. What would be your decision?

(a) Replace now

(b) Replace 1 year later

(c) Replace 2 years later

(d) Replace 3 years later

Solution:

Given: economic service lives for both defender and challenger

Find: when to replace the defender at MARR = 12%

$$PW(12\%)_{n=0} = \frac{\$3,100}{0.12} = \$25,833$$

$$PW(12\%)_{n=1} = [\$3,000 + \$25,833](P/F,12\%,1)$$
$$= \$25,744$$

$$PW(12\%)_{n=2} = \$2,500(P/A,12\%,2) + \$25,833(P/F,12\%,2)$$
$$= \$24,819$$

$$PW(12\%)_{n=3} = \$3,200(P/A,12\%,3) + \$25,833(P/F,12\%,3)$$
$$= \$26,073$$

Keep the defender for 2 years and then replace it with the challenger.

Problem Statement for Questions (11s.9 – 11s.12)

The new machine tool is simply beautiful," exclaimed John Ogletree, industrial engineer for Trent Manufacturing Company. "No wonder the plant manager is so anxious to buy it." "I am not sure it is worth replacing the present machine tool," replied Jerry Hanson, operation manager. "Everyone seems to forget that we purchased our present machine just four years ago at a cost of $12,000. The new tool will cost $15,000. The worst part is that we can only get $2,000 out of old machine tool if we sell it now." "That's quite a loss for the company to absorb." "We can make up the loss very quickly," countered John. "Willow Creek Manufacturing Co. in the northern part of the state says that scrap loss decreased by 20% when they purchased these new tools. I've gathered a lot of information about the new tools, and I will have a recommendation ready for the plant manager tomorrow."

Option 1: You continue to use an old machine tool that was bought 4 years ago for $12,000. It has been fully depreciated but can be sold for $2,000. If kept, it could be used for 3 more years with proper maintenance and with some extra care. No salvage value is expected at the end of 3 years. The maintenance costs would run $10,000 per year for the old machine tool.

Option 2: You purchase a brand-new machine tool at a price of $15,000 to replace the present equipment. Because of the nature of the product manufactured, it also has an expected economic life of 3 years, and will have a salvage value of $5,000 at the end of that time. With the new machine tool, the expected operating and maintenance costs (with the scrap savings) amount to $3,000 each year for 3 years. The allowed depreciation amounts for the new machine are $5,000 during the first year, $6,668 during the second year, and $1,110 (with the half-year convention) during the third year.

The income tax rate is 35%. Any gains will also be taxed at 35%.

11s.9 For the old machine tools, what would be the amount of sunk cost that should be recognized in replacement analysis?

(a) $10,000   (c) $12,000

(b) $2,000   (d) 0

Solution:

Given: $I = \$12,000$ paid 4 years ago, fully depreciated asset, current market value = $2,000

Find: sunk cost related to old machine

Sunk cost $= \$12,000 - \$2,000 = \$10,000$

11s.10 What is the opportunity cost of retaining the old machine tool now?

(a) $700   (c) $2,000

(b) $1,300   (d) $10,000

Solution:

Given: $I = \$12,000$ paid 4 years ago, fully depreciated asset, current market value = $2,000

Find: opportunity cost

The asset has been fully depreciated, so the book value is zero. Net proceeds from sale of the old machine are known as the opportunity cost of keeping the defender.

Opportunity cost $= \$2,000 - (\$2,000 - 0)(0.35) = \$1,300$

11s.11 What would be the net proceeds associated with disposing the new machine tool at the end of 3 years?

(a) $4,028 (c) $972

(b) $2,778 (d) $5,000

Solution:

<u>Given</u>: $I = \$15{,}000$, $D_1 = \$5{,}000$, $D_2 = \$6{,}668$, $D_3 = \$1{,}110$ (with the half-year convention), O&M cost = $3,000 each year, $S = \$5{,}000$, $N = 3$ years
<u>Find</u>: net proceeds from sale of the old machine at $N = 3$

The book value of the challenger at the end of year 3:

$$BV_3 = \$15{,}000 - (\$5{,}000 + \$6{,}668 + \$1{,}110)$$
$$= \$2{,}222$$
$$\text{Taxable Gains} = \$5{,}000 - \$2{,}222 = \$2{,}778$$
$$\text{Gains Tax} = \$2{,}778(0.35) = \$972$$
$$\text{Net proceeds from sale} = \$5{,}000 - \$972 = \$4{,}028$$

11s.12 What is the net incremental benefit or loss in present value associated with replacing the old machine tools at an interest rate of 15%?

(a) $6,648 (c) $421

(b) $2,879 (d) $960

Solution:

<u>Given</u>: financial data as summarized in the following table, MARR = 15%
<u>Find</u>: net incremental benefit (loss) in present value with replacing the defender

	Defender			Challenger		
	Market Value	Dep.	O&M	Market Value	Dep.	O&M
0	$2,000			$15,000		
1			0	10,000	$5,000	$3,000
2			0	10,000	$6,668	3,000
3		0	0	10,000	5,000	$1,110	3,000

Defender

Income Statement	0		1		2		3
Revenue							
Expenses:							
O&M		$	10,000	$	10,000	$	10,000
Depreciation		$	-	$	-	$	-
Taxable income		$	(10,000)	$	(10,000)	$	(10,000)
Income taxes (35%)		$	(3,500)	$	(3,500)	$	(3,500)
Net income		$	(6,500)	$	(6,500)	$	(6,500)

Cash Flow Statement

	0		1		2		3
Cash from operation							
Net income		$	(6,500)	$	(6,500)	$	(6,500)
Depreciation		$	-	$	-	$	-
Cash from investing							
Investment	$ (1,300)						
Salavage value						$	-
Gains taxes						$	-
Net cash flow	$ (1,300)	$	(6,500)	$	(6,500)	$	(6,500)

Challenger

Income Statement	0		1		2		3
Revenue							
Expenses:							
O&M		$	3,000	$	3,000	$	3,000
Depreciation		$	5,000	$	6,668	$	1,110
Taxable income		$	(8,000)	$	(9,668)	$	(4,110)
Income taxes (35%)		$	(2,800)	$	(3,384)	$	(1,439)
Net income		$	(5,200)	$	(6,284)	$	(2,672)

Cash Flow Statement

	0		1		2		3
Cash from operation							
Net income		$	(5,200)	$	(6,284)	$	(2,672)
Depreciation		$	5,000	$	6,668	$	1,110
Cash from investing							
Investment	$ (15,000)						
Salavage value						$	5,000
Gains taxes						$	(972)
Net cash flow	$ (15,000)	$	(200)	$	384	$	2,467

Incremental Cash Flows (Challenger - Defender)

	0		1		2		3
	$ (13,700)	$	6,300	$	6,884	$	8,967

PW(15%) = 2,879.02

Chapter 12 Benefit-Cost Analysis

12s.1 Which of the following statements is <u>incorrect</u>?

(a) Both the PW criterion and the *B/C* ratio allow you to make a consistent accept/reject decision for a given investment as long as you use the same interest rate.

(b) As long as you use a *B/C* ratio as a base to compare mutually exclusive investment alternatives, it should be based on a *B/C* ratio on the incremental investment.

(c) Income taxes are not considered in any public investment analyses.

(d) Income taxes must be considered in evaluating investment projects for nonprofit organizations (such as hospitals and churches).

Solution:

Given: statements related to B/C ratios
Find: the incorrect statement

The answer is (d), as non-profit organizations do not pay income taxes.

12s.2 A city government is considering increasing the capacity of the current wastewater treatment plant. The estimated financial data for the project is as follows:

Description	Data
Capital investment	$1,200,000
Project life	25 years
Incremental annual benefits	$250,000
Incremental annual costs	$100,000
Salvage value	$50,000
Discount rate	6%

What would be the benefit-cost ratio for this expansion project?

(a) 3.26   (b) 3.12

(c) 1.30   (d) 2.23.

Solution:

Given: financial data as summarized above, $i = 6\%$

Find: B/C ratio

$$I = \$1,200,000 - \$50,000(P/F, 6\%, 25) = \$1,188,350$$

$$C' = \$100,000(P/A, 6\%, 25) = \$1,278,336$$

$$B = \$250,000(P/A, 6\%, 25) = \$3,195,839$$

$$BC(6\%) = \frac{B}{I+C'} = \frac{\$3,195,839}{\$1,188,350 + \$1,278,336}$$

$$= 1.30$$

Comments: As a variation to the traditional B/C ratio, you may use the net B/C ratio, which is defined as $BC'(i) = (B - C')/I$. In our example, the net B/C ratio would be

$$BC'(6\%) = \frac{B-C'}{I} = \frac{\$3,195,839 - \$1,278,336}{\$1,188,350}$$

$$= 1.61 > 0$$

This ratio indicates how much benefit the project generates for each dollar of expenditure.

12s.3 Auburn Recreation and Parks Department is considering two mutually exclusive proposals for a new softball complex on a city-owned lot.

Alternative Required Benefits	Seating Costs	Annual Design Investment	Annual Capacity
A1	3,000	$194,000	$87,500
$800,000			
A2	4,000	224,000	105,000
1,000,000			

The complex will be useful for 30 years and has no appreciable salvage value (regardless of seating capacity). Assuming an 8% discount rate, which of the following statements is <u>incorrect</u>?

(a) Select A1 because it has the largest *B/C* ratio.

(b) Select A1 because it has the most benefits per seating capacity.

(c) Select A1 because it has the largest PW.

(d) Select A1 because the incremental benefits generated from A2 are not large enough to offset the additional investment ($200,000 over A1).

Solution:

Given: financial data as summarized above

Find: the incorrect statement

Approach: We must use incremental investment approach in comparing alternatives. To apply incremental analysis, we compute the incremental differences for each term (B, I, C') and take the B/C ratio based on these differences.

Alternative	I	C'	B	B/C ratio	PW(8%)
A1	$800,000	$985,056	$2,184,010	1.22	$398,954
A2	1,000,000	1,182,067	2,521,744	1.16	339,677
A2 – A1	$200,000	197,011	337,734	0.85	-$59,277

Clearly, A1 is a better choice. Even the B/C ratio for A1 happens to exceed that of A2; we should not select the project based on the magnitude of B/C ratio alone. We should apply the incremental analysis to select the correct alternative. Since $BC(8\%)_{A2-A1} = 0.85 < 1$, A1 is a better alternative. The answer is (a), because A1 is selected with a wrong reason.

12s.4 The City of Jefferson is reviewing the benefits and costs of a potential universal   water-metering program. Two options are considered:

- **Option 1 – Treated Surface Water Only**
  Benefits of Deferring/Downsizing Water and Sewer Projects - $28.1 million
  Costs of Metering - $9.3 million
  Benefit-Cost Ratio – 3.02

- **Option 2 – Treated Surface Water Supplemented By 40 ML/Day Groundwater**
  Benefits of Deferring/Downsizing Water and Sewer Projects - $38.9 million
  Costs of Metering (and groundwater development) - $14.7 million
  Benefit-Cost Ratio – 2.65

Which option should the city implement, assuming that the city has enough money to fund either project?

Solution:

Given: financial data as summarized above

Find: which option to fund

Approach: Both options are acceptable as their B/C ratios exceed 1. To find the correct alternative, apply the incremental analysis.

Alternative	$I + C'$	B	B/C ratio	$PW = B - (I+C')$
Option 1	$9.3 million	$28.1 million	3.02	$18.8 million
Option 2	$14.7 million	$38.9 million	2.65	$24.2 million
2 – 1	$5.4 million	$10.80 million	2.00	$5.40 million

With $BC_{2-1} > 1$, Option 2 becomes the better choice.

12s.5 A municipal city is trying to decide whether to build a parking garage. An engineering plan calculates that the building will cost $2 million and that it will cost $200,000 per year to operate. Our analysis of operating revenue determines that the garage will start to earn revenues of $500,000 per year starting in the second year. The city is interested in knowing whether this project will be profitable over the next eight years at 6%. If not, how long the city has to wait to breakeven.

Solution:

Given: $I = \$2,000,000$, annual revenue = $500,000, annual operating cost = $200,000, $i = 6\%$

Find: (1) profitable over a 8-year period of operation, (2) how long does it to breakeven?

Approach: Compute the B/C ratio at 6% over a 8-year period of operation to find whether the ratio exceed 1. If not, determine *when* to breakeven, meaning that $BC(6\%) = 1$.

- First 8-year operation:

$$I = \$2,000,000$$
$$C' = \$200,000(P/A,10\%,8) = \$1,066,985$$
$$B = \$500,000(P/A,10\%,8) = \$2,667,463$$
$$BC(6\%) = \frac{B}{I+C'} = \frac{\$2,667,463}{\$2,000,000+\$1,066,985}$$
$$= 0.87 < 1 \quad \text{(not profitable yet)}$$

- For a 12-year period of operation, $BC(10\%) = 1.02$. In other words, it will take about 12 years to breakeven.

12s.6 A state is interested in improving accident prevention counter measures on state public highways and bridges. The following set of projects has been recommended for evaluation at three different locations and assumes the budget is $20 million. All alternatives are mutually <u>independent</u> projects.

Location	Alternative	Benefit ($B - C'$)	Cost (I)	B/C Ratio
I	I-A	$45	12	3.75
	I-B	30	9	3.33
II	II-A	35	6	5.83
	II-B	20	12	1.67
III	III-A	25	2	12.5
	III-B	30	7	4.29

Determine the best combination of projects within the budget constraint.

Solution:

Given: six projects to consider, budget = $20 million

Find: the combinations of projects that maximize the total benefit

Approach: If there were no budget constraint, all projects would be selected. However, with the budget constraint, we may eliminate any dominated projects from the list. For example, when we compare I-A with II-B, both projects cost the same, but I-A brings in a larger benefit, so I-A dominates II-B. So we can drop II-B from the list. When we compare I-B with III-B, both projects generate the same amount of benefit, but I-B costs more than III-B. So we also drop I-B from the list. The non-dominated set is (I-A, II-A, III-A, and III-B).

Location	Alternative	Benefit ($B - C'$)	Cost (I)	B/C Ratio
I	I-A	$45	12	3.75
II	II-A	35	6	5.83
III	III-A	25	2	12.5
	III-B	30	7	4.29

The best combination is (I-A, II-A, III-B). It gives the total benefit in the amount of $110 million and costs just $19 million.

Chapter 13 Understanding Financial Statements

13s.1 True-False Questions:

[ ] 1. The balance sheet statement summarizes how much the firm owns as well as owes for a typical operating period.

[ ] 2. The income statement summarizes the net income produced by the corporation at a specified reporting date.

[ ] 3. The cash flow statement summarizes how the corporation generated cash during the operating period.

[ ] 4. Working capital measures the company's ability to repay current liabilities using only current assets.

[ ] 5. The days sales outstanding (DSO) represents the average length of time that the firm must wait after making a sale before receiving cash.

[ ] 6. The lower debt ratio, the greater the protection afforded creditors in the event of liquidation.

[ ] 7. P/E ratios are higher for firms with high growth prospects, other things held constant, but they are lower for riskier firms.

[ ] 8. Higher market/book (MB) ratios are generally associated with firms that have a high rate of return on common equity.

[ ] 9. A high quick ratio is always a good indication of a well-managed liquidity position.

[ ] 10. A decline in inventory turnover ratio suggests that the firm's liquidity position is improving.

[ ] 11. The profit margin on sales is calculated by dividing net operating income by sales

[ ] 12 When a corporation buys back its own stock, this is called Treasury Stock. The firm's cash and equity are both reduced.

Solution:

[F] 1. The balance sheet statement summarizes how much the firm owns as well as owes for <u>a typical operating period</u>. (Note: a specified reporting period)

[F] 2. The income statement summarizes the net income produced by the corporation at a <u>specified reporting date</u>. (Note: a typical operating period)

[F] 3. The cash flow statement summarizes how the corporation generated cash during the operating period. <u>Note: It summarizes how the company generates its cash and where it spent during the reporting period.</u>

[T] 4. Working capital measures the company's ability to repay current liabilities using only current assets.

[T] 5. The days sales outstanding (DSO) represents the average length of time that the firm must wait after making a sale before receiving cash.

[T] 6. The lower debt ratio, the greater the protection afforded creditors in the event of liquidation.

[T] 7. P/E ratios are higher for firms with high growth prospects, other things held constant, but they are lower for riskier firms.

[T] 8. Higher market/book (MB) ratios are generally associated with firms that have a high rate of return on common equity.

[F] 9. A high quick ratio is always a good indication of a well-managed liquidity position. Note: Excess cash resulting from poor management could produce a high quick ratio. Similarly, if accounts receivable are not collected promptly, this could also lead to a high quick ratio

[F] 10. A decline in inventory turnover ratio suggests that the firm's liquidity position is improving. Note: A decline in inventory turnover ratio indicates that it takes longer to liquidate inventory.

[F] 11. The profit margin on sales is calculated by dividing net operating income by sales
(Note: net income rather than operating income)

[T] 12 When a corporation buys back its own stock, this is called Treasury Stock. The firm's cash and equity are both reduced.

13s.2 Which of the following statements is most correct?

(a) Generally, firms with high profit margins have high asset turnover ratios.

(b) Having a high current ratio and a high quick ratio is always a good indication a firm is managing its liquidity position well.

(c) Knowing that return on assets (ROA) measures the firm's effective utilization of assets without considering how these assets are financed, two firms with the same EBIT must have the same ROA.

(d) One way to improve the current ratio is to use cash to pay off current liabilities.

Solution:

Statement (a) is just reverse of what actually occurs. Firms with high profit margins have low turnover ratios and vice versa. Statement (b) is false, as excess cash resulting from poor management could produce a high quick ratio. Statement (c) is also false, as two firms with the same EBIT do not necessarily have the same total assets. Statement (d) is correct—whenever the same amount of reduction in the numerator and denominator, the ratio is increasing.

13S.3 The following data apply to Fisher & Company (millions of dollars except ratio figures):

- Cash and marketable securities $100
- Fixed assets $280
- Sales $1,200
- Net income $358
- Inventory $180
- Current ratio   3.2
- Average collection period   45 days
- Average common equity $500

Find Fisher's

  (a) Accounts receivable

  (b) Current assets

  (c) Current liabilities

  (d) Total assets

  (e) Long-term debt

  (f) Profit margin

Solution:

  (a) Accounts receivable:

$$\text{Average collection period} = \frac{\text{A/R}}{\text{Annual Sales}/365}$$

$$= \frac{\text{A/R}}{\$1,200/365}$$

$$= 45 \text{ days}$$

$$\text{A/R} = 45(1200/365) = \$147.95$$

  (b) Current assets:

$$\text{Current assets} = \text{Cash and marketable securities} + \text{A/R} + \text{Inventory}$$

$$= \$100 + 148 + \$180 = \$428$$

  (c) Current liabilities

$$\text{Current ratio} = \frac{\text{Current assets}}{\text{Current liabilities}} = \frac{\$428}{\text{Current liabilities}} = 3.2$$

$$\text{Current liabilities} = \$428/3.2 = \$134$$

(d) Total assets

$$\text{Total assets} = \text{Currrent assets} + \text{Fixed assets} = \$428 + \$280$$
$$= \$708$$

(e) Long-term debt

$$\text{Total assets} = \text{Currrent assets} + \text{Fixed assets} = \$428 + \$280$$
$$= \$708$$

$$\text{Total assets} = \text{Common equity} + \text{Current liabilities} + \text{Long-term debt}$$
$$\$708 = \$500 + \$134 + \text{Long-term liabilities}$$
$$\text{Long-term liabilities} = \$74$$

(f) Profit margin

$$\text{Profit-margin} = \frac{\text{Net income}}{\text{Net sales}} = \frac{\$358}{\$1,200} = 30\%$$

The following financial statements apply to the next six problems, 13s.4 – 13s.10.

Inland Manufacturing Balance Sheet
(Dollars in Millions)

	December 31, 2003	December 31, 2002
Cash	$ 400	$ 300
Account Receivables	560	450
Inventory	790	550
Total current assets	$1,750	$1,300
Total fixed assets	1,200	1,210
Total assets	$2,950	$2,510
Account payable	$ 350	$ 250
Note payable	470	330
Other current liabilities	220	130
Total current liabilities	$1,040	$ 710

Long-term debt	580	580
Common equity	$1,330	$1,220
Total liabilities and equity	$2,950	$2,510

Inland Manufacturing Income Statement
December 31, 2003
(Dollars in Millions)

Gross sales		$2,450
Cost of goods sold:		
Materials	$230	
Labor	850	
Overhead	230	
Depreciation	400	$1,710
Gross profit		$ 740
Selling expenses		40
General and administrative expenses		60
Earnings before interest and taxes (EBIT)		$ 640
Interest expenses		25
Earnings before income taxes		$ 615
Provision for income taxes (40%)		246
Net income		$ 369

13s.4 Calculate the liquidity ratios, that is, current and the quick ratios.

Solution:

$$\text{Current ratio} = \frac{\text{Current assets}}{\text{Current liabilities}} = \frac{\$1,750}{\$1,040} = 1.68$$

$$\text{Quick ratio} = \frac{\text{Current assets - Inventory}}{\text{Current liabilities}} = \frac{\$1,750 - \$790}{\$1,040} = 0.92$$

13s.5 Calculate the debt management ratios, that is, the debt and times-interest-earned ratios.

Solution:

$$\text{Debt ratio} = \frac{\text{Total debt}}{\text{Total assets}} = \frac{\$\$1,620}{\$2,950} = 0.55$$

$$\text{Times-interest-earned ratio} = \frac{\text{EBIT}}{\text{Interest expense}} = \frac{\$640 + \$25}{\$25} = 26.60$$

13s.6 Calculate the asset management ratios, that is, the inventory turnover ratios, total asset turnover ratio, and days sales outstanding.

Solution:

$$\text{Inventory turnover ratio} = \frac{\text{Sales}}{\text{Average inventory}} = \frac{\$2,450}{(\$790 + \$550)/2} = 3.66 \text{ times}$$

$$\text{Total asset turnover ratio} = \frac{\text{Sales}}{\text{Total assets}} = \frac{\$2,450}{\$\$2,950} = 0.83 \text{ times}$$

$$\text{Days Sales Outstanding} = \frac{\text{Accounts receivable}}{\text{Average sales per day}} = \frac{\$560}{\$2,450/365} = 83.43 \text{ days}$$

13s.7 Calculate the profitability ratios, that is, the profit margin on sales, return on total assets, and return on common equity.

Solution:

$$\text{Profit margin on sales} = \frac{\text{Net income}}{\text{Sales}} = \frac{\$369}{\$2,450} = 15\%$$

$$\text{Return on total assets} = \frac{\text{Net income} + \text{Interest expense (1 - tax rate)}}{\text{Average total assets}}$$

$$= \frac{\$369 + \$25(1 - 0.40)}{(\$2,510 + \$2,950)/2} = 14\%$$

$$\text{Return on equity} = \frac{\text{Net income}}{\text{Average common equity}} = \frac{\$369}{(\$1,330 + \$1,220)/2} = 29\%$$

13s.8 Calculate the market value ratios, that is, the price/earnings ratio and the market/book value ratio. Inland had an average of 100 million shares outstanding during 2003, and the stock price on December 31, 2003, was $35.

Solution:

$$\text{P/E ratio} = \frac{\text{Market price per share}}{\text{Earnings per share}} = \frac{\$35}{\$369/100} = 9.49$$

$$\text{Book value} = \frac{\text{Total stockholder'sequity - Preferred stock}}{\text{Shares outstanding}}$$

$$= \frac{\$1,330 - 0}{100} = \$13.30$$

$$\text{Market/BV} = \frac{\$35 \text{ per share}}{\$13.30 \text{ per share}} = 2.63$$

13s.9 If Inland uses $350 of cash to pay off $350 of its accounts payable, what is the new current ratio after this action?

Solution:

Current ratio before action = 1.68

$$\text{Current ratio after action} = \frac{\$1,750 - \$350}{\$1,040 - \$350} = 2.03$$

13s.10 If Inland uses its $400 cash balance to pay off $400 of its long-term debt, what will be its new current ratio?

Solution:

Current ratio before action = 1.68

$$\text{Current ratio after action} = \frac{\$1,750 - \$350}{\$1,040} = 1.35$$
